Ross made a curious little sound in his throat and his hands slid from her shoulders and down her arms, his fingers painfully hard. But this time she was not afraid. His eyes seemed drawn to the quivering lips. Hers were focused with equal intensity on his well-shaped mouth. She had never expected to long like this again for a man's kiss.

There was a sudden tension in the atmosphere, but now it was not one of anger or of fear. The silence seemed charged with electricity. Warmth invaded Claire's body and her face. Her mouth was dry and the glitter of tears in her eyes was replaced by something else, something feverish and yearning.

It seemed to her that Ross's head was moving closer. With a little sigh, she closed her eyes and, her lips pouting an unconscious invitation, she swayed towards him.

'No!' The word exploded with violence from him. He pushed away. Her eyes flew open as he stood up and turned his back on her.

'Ross?' she enquired tremulously.

'I'm sorry, Claire,' he said stiffly, 'but you seemed to be under the impression that I was about to kiss you.'

'Well, weren't you?' she challenged.

'*No!*'

TIRED OF KISSING

BY

ANNABEL MURRAY

MILLS & BOON LIMITED
ETON HOUSE   18-24 PARADISE ROAD
RICHMOND   SURREY   TW9 1SR

First published in Great Britain 1991
by Mills & Boon Limited

© Annabel Murray 1991

Australian copyright 1991
Philippine copyright 1991
This edition 1991

ISBN 0 263 77364 7

Set in Times Roman 10½ on 11½ pt.
01-9112-53006 C

Made and printed in Great Britain

For Amy,
even though she's too young to read it yet.

CHAPTER ONE

'But why Provence?' Claire persisted. There was more animation in her voice and her small, heart-shaped face had lost some of its recent strain, her cousin thought.

Wanda, at the wheel of the spanking new motor-caravan, shrugged evasively. 'Why not Provence?'

Buying a motor-caravan had originally been Claire's idea. A lot of her work as a make-up artist took her on outdoor locations, so it would be very useful to have her own mobile accommodation. Unfortunately there had been no way she could afford it—not until the flat she now loathed was sold.

But Wanda had seemed much struck by the notion. 'Fantastic! You could go anywhere you liked whenever you liked. There are no end of caravan sites—in this country and abroad.' And the notion of the trip to France had been Wanda's, including the suggestion that Claire should accompany her.

'What you need, my pet, is a change of scenery. A holiday—preferably a long, exotic one.'

Claire was still puzzled by Wanda's seeming insistence. True, Wanda had been kind and supportive of late, but Claire believed that was simply family loyalty, since they had never been friends in the real sense of the word. Wanda was older, for one thing, and they had never had much in common. As a child, Claire had never really been sure she liked her cousin. There were certain spiteful little tricks she could not forget.

But perhaps she was being unfair. Spiteful children, she supposed, could grow up to be caring adults.

'You're probably right,' she'd told her cousin. 'I *could* do with a break. But I may not be able to afford holidays in future.'

'Rubbish!' Wanda Hedley had been briskly dismissive. 'You can't afford *not* to have a break. Just look at yourself! You're a pale, thin ghost of yourself. For months now you've been on the verge of cracking up—and who can blame you? That pig of a man! He should be shot. Look, I know work is the only thing that's kept you going. But it's all over now, so relax for a few weeks. Have fun. Learn to laugh again.'

Yes, it was all over, her brief but disastrous marriage. For exactly twelve months she'd been Claire O'Reilly—Joe's wife. That year had seemed like ten. And now—now she was Claire Lovejoy once more. She did not even want her ex-husband's name to remind her of him.

But would she ever be able to forget? Those twelve months had left scars she felt would be with her for a lifetime.

'I'd like to come to France,' she'd told Wanda again. 'But I told you, I can't afford it. Air fares, hotel bills—and,' warningly, as the older girl had parted her lips to speak, 'I'm not going to sponge off you, so please don't suggest it.'

'I wasn't going to. What I had in mind was——'

'And I couldn't afford to repay a loan either.'

'Claire! Will you shut up for a moment and listen? You said you'd like to buy a mobile home, right? Why don't *I* buy it—initially, that is? We'll use it to go abroad. No air fares, no hotel bills. And then, when you sell your flat, you *will* be able to repay me, and you'll have your new home.'

Claire had been struck by her cousin's unexpected generosity. Wanda could well afford the money, of course. But even so...

'Well?' Wanda had demanded impatiently.

'Yes!' Claire had said. 'Oh, yes—and thanks, Wanda. You're a brick, you really are. I can't tell you how grateful I am.'

'Save it!' Wanda had declared brusquely. 'I'll call in the debt some time. You can count on that.'

'Got over your seasickness yet?' Wanda asked now.

'Yes—thank goodness.'

The Channel crossing had been horribly choppy and the ferry's bar crowded and smoky. Claire rarely drank alcohol and she loathed the smell of tobacco, but she hadn't wanted to be a wet blanket. After all, this was Wanda's holiday, and like a lot of journalists her cousin drank and smoked heavily. Nevertheless, Claire had been glad when the order came to return to their vehicles and they'd driven off the ferry on to French soil.

The drive down through France was proving to be a fascinating if tiring experience. Claire had never been to France before. Nor was she used to driving such long distances, and it had been a relief when Wanda took over the wheel once more, giving Claire leisure to observe her surroundings.

According to Wanda there was a parking site in the vicinity of Puit de Mirabeau, their eventual destination.

'But we shan't get there tonight,' she told Claire. 'We'll make an overnight stop somewhere and reach Puit de Mirabeau mid-morning tomorrow.'

From the little Wanda had told her, Puit de Mirabeau didn't sound much like a holiday resort.

'Are you *sure* this trip isn't work?' Claire probed again.

'I *told* you! *No!*' Wanda sounded snappy. But then she was driving an unfamiliar vehicle, in heavy traffic—and on the "wrong side of the road". Claire decided to postpone any further questions.

It didn't really matter where they were going or why. She was just glad she'd acceded to Wanda's plan.

'Well, isn't this better than work?' Wanda asked unexpectedly, almost as though she'd read her cousin's thoughts.

'Yes. Though I wouldn't ever want to give it up completely. But it is wonderful, just for a while, to be free of routine. Most of all,' Claire said feelingly, 'it's great to be able to call my soul my own—to come and go as I please.'

'No Joe clocking you in and out,' Wanda said understandingly.

For life with Joe had been one long inquisition. 'Where are you going? Who with? How long will you be?' He'd even got into the habit of ringing her at work two or three times a day on various pretexts, checking that she was where she said she'd be. He'd even been suspicious and critical of her women friends. He'd been eating her alive.

'Joe always expected me to come straight home from work,' she explained to Wanda now. 'And if I was going to be late I had to phone, to justify the delay. In the end, I found myself telling white lies because it was easier.'

'Why not?' Wanda said cheerfully. 'I tell 'em all the time—especially to the aged parents. What they don't know can't worry 'em.'

Claire frowned a little. Personally she hated deception, and she was very fond of her aunt and uncle.

Only a fortnight ago she had gone down to Hertfordshire with her cousin, to visit Wanda's parents, and as always she had experienced a pang at the sight of her mother's identical twin. Claire often envied her cousin for having both parents still alive. Her own had been killed nearly two years ago in a multiple motorway crash.

But she had been surprised when her cousin announced her intention of paying a weekend visit and invited Claire to accompany her. Wanda did not often go to see her parents. In fact, Wanda's whole behaviour of late had been a bit of a surprise.

Unexpectedly it had been her cousin who had provided the moral support Claire needed during the final bitter break-up of her marriage and the divorce proceedings. Wanda was not normally given to considering others. Her cousin had a hard, selfish streak which, admittedly, had stood her in good stead in her career. But Claire knew that a few people had been trampled beneath Wanda's elegant feet on her way to the top.

Still, Wanda had been kind to Claire—a case, Claire supposed, of blood being thicker than water. As they came out of court that final morning she'd thanked her cousin.

'What for, for heaven's sake?' Wanda had demurred.

'For everything. You've been marvellous these past few months. I owe you.'

'I may hold you to that,' Wanda had said—lightly enough, but there had been an expression in her pale blue eyes which did not match her tone, and Claire had experienced a sudden inexplicable feeling of unease. An unease she had immediately brushed aside. Living with Joe, she'd decided, must have made her nearly as twisted as he was, if she was now looking for ulterior motives in her cousin's kindness.

'Mum's having a bit of a party,' Wanda had enlarged on her invitation. 'And you know Mum and her parties.'

'I certainly do. They're not to be missed.'

Alice Hedley had recently been made chairman of her local writers' circle. Proud of her talented and successful daughter, she had asked Wanda to come down and give the group a talk on journalism. Wanda hadn't been able to get away from London and her work on a weekday, so Alice Hedley had arranged a special meeting in her own home.

Though Claire had willingly accepted her cousin's invitation she hadn't been quite so sure about the idea of the party. Once upon a time she had looked forward to social gatherings of the type her aunt enjoyed, the stimulating conversation of intellectual people. Once she too had sparkled in good company, revelling in the society of men and women alike.

Joe had spoiled all that for her. His possessive jealousy had suffocated her spontaneity, made her self-conscious, afraid to talk to other men, let alone smile at them or appear to enjoy their company.

Unlike her late sister, Alice Hedley was buoyantly gregarious. Her house always seemed to be bursting at the seams with people, and that weekend had been no exception.

Wanda had two brothers and two sisters who always seemed to be visiting with their partners and various progeny. Claire had often thought it must be nice to be part of a large, loving family. Because of her own solitary childhood, she had always wanted to have several children. But that was a dream Joe had demolished. It was as if he could not bear to share her attention with anyone, not even his own baby. That weekend, drawn into the noise and warmth of family life, Claire, for the first time in a long while, had felt herself beginning to relax.

'It was really great, the other weekend, seeing Auntie Alice and all the family,' she said wistfully now.

'She enjoyed having you. And it was certainly better for you than moping about in that tacky little flat.'

Wanda had always been disdainful about the comfortable but undeniably modest apartment that had been the O'Reillys' home. By Wanda's standards, Claire recognised, it must have seemed a hovel. Her cousin, her senior by some six years, had made herself a successful career as a freelance journalist. In addition she was now the features editor for one of the more prestigious glossy magazines.

'We can't all afford luxury penthouses by the River Thames,' Claire retorted.

'Flat hasn't sold yet, I suppose?' Wanda asked.

'No, worse luck.' How she hated that flat! What should have been a home had become a prison, and Joe her gaoler. 'I'll be glad to get shot of it. Apart from anything else, it's keeping me broke. Even with two salaries coming in, we could only just manage the mortgage repayments.'

'Looks as though we're going to be lucky with the weather,' Wanda commented a little while later. With many long miles still ahead of them, they had stopped near a low ridge of hills for a picnic lunch.

'Yes.' But in fact Claire found the sun a little too hot. She had the delicate complexion that went with her auburn hair. And the sun that was scorching the evergreen shrubs also reflected starkly off the sur-rounding rocks. Orange butterflies flapped lethargically over the flowers and roadside Forestry Commission notices warned of the dangers of fire.

'You enjoyed seeing the family,' Wanda referred once more to the weekend they'd shared, 'but,' and she laughed, 'you weren't quite so sure about some of Mum's cronies, were you? You made quite a hit with the men—not that you took any advantage of that.'

'I used to be more outgoing,' Claire confessed. 'But these days I'm afraid to act in even the most innocent friendly manner, in case men think I'm being too forward.'

'That bloody Joe!' Wanda exclaimed. 'He really gave you a complex, didn't he? Why the hell did you ever marry him in the first place?'

'I've thought about that a lot lately,' Claire admitted. 'I met him just after Mum and Dad were killed. I suppose it was a dangerous time to get involved with a man. I was so devastated, so lonely— I felt I had no one of my own. And he was so different when I first met him. He was good-looking, amusing, and so attentive. He seemed to be everything I wanted. I just fell head over heels. I couldn't have known how much marriage would change him.'

'It probably didn't,' Wanda said shrewdly. 'He was probably doing a good cover-up job, until he'd got you where he wanted you. But just remember, you're shot of the rat now. And you're looking better already. Which just goes to prove there *is* life after Joe! Life after Joe,' she repeated thoughtfully. 'That would make a damned good title for an article.'

'You won't write about me and Joe, though, will you?' Claire said anxiously. It had never dawned on her that Wanda might see her story as "copy".

Wanda laughed. 'Don't worry, pet. I'm on the scent of a much more fascinating story.'

'Oh?' Watching her cousin's profile, Claire's green eyes were expectant. Wanda had interviewed some very interesting people in her time. 'Do tell,' she invited.

But Wanda tapped the side of her long aquiline nose—a nose that someone had once described as perfect for poking into other people's business. 'Sorry! Top secret—even from you. And besides,' she added in what sounded suspiciously like an afterthought, 'I'm on holiday right now. Forget Joe,' Wanda went on. 'You've got to start living normally again. That weekend was a good start, even if you didn't fancy any of the men. And there were some decentish types, I noticed. Not all writers' circles, thank God, are composed of little old ladies in woolly hats and twin sets.'

'I wouldn't have minded if it had been an all-female do,' Claire said wryly. 'As you realised, I'm not actively looking for male company.'

'Give it time,' Wanda advised. 'You'll meet someone else—you're bound to. How about a nice holiday romance? Here in France?'

Claire smiled but shook her head. 'Too soon. Besides, I'm not sure I *want* to meet anyone else.'

'Damn it Claire, not every man is a Joe O'Reilly. He was paranoid!'

Yes, Joe *had* been paranoid. Despite the unhappiness he had caused her, Claire was charitable enough to admit that his had been a sickness, stemming from an emotional immaturity she had not discovered until after they were married.

'Your mum's friends *were* a nice crowd,' she agreed now. 'And I did enjoy meeting them.' There'd been about forty people, and even though the Hedleys had knocked their two ground-floor rooms into one it had been a tight squeeze. 'And your talk went well.'

Wanda had a witty, often malicious tongue and she had plenty of entertaining material concerning the foibles of the famous. Claire's own work as a make-up artist had taken her into the world of celebrities. But TV stars and politicians did not confide their innermost secrets to the almost faceless person who powdered their noses.

'The talk was OK, I suppose,' Wanda agreed. 'It's all a bit of a bore really. But I'm so used to doing them I just go on to automatic pilot. And the questions are so puerile and predictable.'

There'd been one question, though, Claire thought now, that Wanda hadn't seemed prepared for, and frankly her cousin's reaction to it had puzzled her.

'Did you ever try to interview Graison Martell?' The question had come from a young, fluffy blonde in tones of evident hero-worship.

There'd been an appreciably longer pause than usual before Wanda answered, almost curtly, 'Mr Martell doesn't . . . didn't like giving interviews.' And then, without enlarging on her statement, as she'd done in the case of other questions, she'd moved on, acknowledging a raised hand from elsewhere in the room.

Claire had stopped listening at that point. The mention of Graison Martell had set her off on a far more interesting train of thought than the fraught subject of whether one should or should not duplicate submissions to editors. Although she'd seen newspaper stories about him, she'd never met Graison Martell in the flesh. Film stars were not as yet within her range of work—though she lived in hopes.

For years Graison Martell had been just about the hottest box-office draw, with his distinctive blond hair and—female reporters said—startlingly blue eyes that made them go weak at the knees.

Claire had never been given to hero-worship herself and she couldn't really understand what it was that made young girls scream and faint at the sight of such men. And their mothers—even some grandmothers, apparently—were equally foolish.

Graison Martell was said to have a reputation for reclusiveness, even though he had spent fifteen years working in the neurotically gregarious society of the film business. Because of his looks he was always cast as the romantic lead, and it was said actresses made their agents' lives a misery in their clamour to play opposite him.

And then, at the height of his success, he had suddenly dropped out of sight. There had been the usual speculation about his reasons, ranging from a story about a disagreement over money to the rumour that he had contracted a terminal illness. But nobody really seemed to know the truth. There had been reported sightings in various parts of the world, but none of them had been confirmed. Graison Martell, whatever his reasons for disappearing, had covered his tracks well.

'On the subject of holiday romances——' Wanda's voice broke in on Claire's reminiscences, but Claire cut her short.

'We've disposed of that topic. I'm not in the market for——'

'But I might be,' Wanda said. 'And,' she teased, 'what about the hand of fate? What about the dreaded Bella's predictions?'

'Oh, that nonsense!' Claire laughed. 'Surely a hard-headed journalist like you doesn't give any credence to that sort of stuff?' She could laugh about it now, though she had not been amused at the time.

Following Wanda's talk to the Writers' Circle, refreshments had been served and conversation became general. Claire found herself accosted by a large plump lady, dressed in an assortment of flowing garments and scarves.

'I've been watching you all evening, my dear. Such an interesting face! Such tragic eyes. I wonder, would you mind . . .?' And before an astonished Claire could say yes or no, the plump one had seized her hand and was concentrating on her palm.

'I wish you could have seen your face!' said Wanda. 'And I wish I'd been close enough to hear what she told you. Writers' circles—like most of the arts—seem to attract the odd crank. But Mum claims that Bella is absolutely brilliant. That she's done everyone in the circle and that it was uncanny how right she was. What *did* she say to put the wind up you? You've never said.'

Claire was evasive. 'Oh, just a lot of nonsense. She seems to fancy herself as a fortune-teller.'

Wanda laughed. 'Don't let Mum hear you say that! She'd consider it sacrilege. Bella is a *palmist*—quite, quite different, according to Mum. Much more scientific.'

'I tried to shut her up,' Claire said. 'Tried to tell her I don't believe in that sort of thing. But she was unstoppable.'

'Well, what did she say?' Wanda demanded.

'Oh, all the usual things. I suppose they all say much the same. That I had an interesting face and an interesting hand. She told me I had emotional warmth

and an affectionate nature but that they'd been stifled.
Oh, and that the shape of my thumb showed I had
feelings of insecurity and self-doubt.'

'Pretty accurate so far. Well,' encouragingly, 'go
on.'

Reluctantly, Claire complied. 'She said I had a long
healthy life-line.'

'Nothing to complain about there. And? There's
more, I know there is.'

'She said my hollow palm meant emotional ups and
downs. And then…and then she started talking about
the marriage line.'

It was at that point that Claire had tried once more
to withdraw her hand. But the other's grasp had been
too strong.

'What did she say about your marriage line?'
Wanda pressed.

'That there was a break,' Claire said reluctantly.
'The end of a relationship after a very short period.
And . . . and she said she saw another romance, a very
deep one, soon after. That's . . . that's all.'

'And *that's* what had you all white-faced and
shaky?' Wanda asked incredulously.

Claire nodded. She had probably mortally offended the plump Bella, when she'd forcibly broken
free and moved away, but she hadn't wanted to hear
cosy predictions about love and romance. It was all
a con trick, anyway. Bella had probably heard all
about Claire's marriage and divorce from Alice
Hedley. The rest was pure conjecture, no more accurate than the daily horoscopes some women avidly
devoured.

'Has she ever read your palm, Wanda?' she asked
curiously.

Wanda grimaced. 'Yes. I'm afraid the silly old bat wasn't very flattering about me. She told me I was a devious opportunist, more interested in power than passion. That I was logical rather than warm-hearted and that I was unscrupulous and destructive. Like you, I think it's a load of old twaddle.' She began to pack up their picnic things. 'Shall we move on? Your turn to drive. Next stop will be for the night.'

It had been during that weekend in Hertfordshire that Wanda had first suggested Provence, enlisting Alice's aid.

'Mum, don't you think Claire should get away for a bit—right away, I mean?'

Alice had been in full agreement. 'Couldn't she go with you, the week after next, to... Where is it you're going, Wanda, dear? I can never remember these foreign names.'

'Puit de Mirabeau—in Provence.'

'Is that your next assignment?' Claire had asked. She knew Wanda often had to travel abroad to interview some of her subjects.

'No.' Wanda had been short. 'Just a holiday. Even editors are allowed them occasionally.'

'Why not go, Claire, dear?' Alice had pressed. 'Being a freelance, it's not as if you have to ask anyone for permission.'

'And you said yourself you had nothing scheduled for the next week or two,' Wanda pointed out.

It occurred to Claire as they drove on that Wanda had said very little about the area she had chosen for her holiday. Nor had Claire any idea how Wanda liked to spend her time. She questioned her now, but her cousin was offhand, almost as if she did not really care.

'Oh, sightseeing, I suppose. You brought your beloved camera, didn't you?' Wanda always declared she couldn't be bothered with photography.

Claire nodded. Photography was her passion, a hobby she would have liked more time to indulge.

'I believe Puit de Mirabeau is a bit of a dump,' Wanda warned. 'But we can use it as a jumping-off place. And there'll be sunbathing—and cycling, of course.' The girls had taken advantage of the caravan's spacious proportions to bring bicycles.

It all seemed a very unsophisticated holiday for her sophisticated cousin, Claire thought doubtfully, convinced that Wanda would be heartily bored before their three weeks were up. She was used to simple holidays, but she just couldn't see her cousin roughing it. Even Wanda's clothes and heavyish make-up did not seem suitable for the month ahead of them.

While Wanda could dress as glamorously as those she interviewed, Claire was used to dressing simply. Her working clothes mostly consisted of a sweater, jeans and soft comfortable shoes, with the addition— on outdoor locations—of an anorak, Wellingtons and a thermal vest. She used very little in the way of cosmetics. A make-up artist seldom had time during the course of the day to attend to her own face.

'I still think you're a brick, to let me tag along on your holiday,' she said now. 'You must be sick of the sight of me after all these months of holding my hand. It's time I stood on my own two feet.'

Wanda shrugged. 'You don't have to be dependent on me once we get there. We can each go our own way if you like. But I would be glad of your company some of the time. I'd asked a...a friend originally, but the arrangement fell through. And my French isn't that good.'

A friend? A man friend? Claire wondered. Wanda seemed to have a vast acquaintance of men. She never had any difficulty in producing an escort when the occasion arose. But invariably they were married men. Wanda had once declared that she much preferred other people's husbands to having one of her own. 'Less trouble, my dear.'

By the time they reached their overnight parking stop both girls were tired and glad to roll into their comfortable bunks. Wanda fell asleep almost immediately, but for months now Claire had found sleep elusive, and lying awake it was all too easy to brood on the past.

Her disillusionment with her marriage had begun on the second day of their honeymoon. Because Joe, a commercial traveller, did not command a very large salary, they had chosen a modest hotel on the south coast. It was a far cry from the exotic setting Claire had always dreamed of. But even daydreamers had their practical side, and anywhere, she'd told herself, could be romantic when you were in love.

Though the hotel was not very large, it did boast a cabaret in the evenings, or some other entertainment. The week the O'Reillys were there it was a nightly talent contest. Some of the contestants came in from outside, some were resident in the hotel.

Claire had always loved to sing, and for her diminutive size she had a large voice, a deep rich contralto. She had sensed a certain reluctance on Joe's part when she asked if he would mind her entering the contest. But he had not actually dissuaded her, and she won the heat for that evening. When the result was announced and she went up to collect her prize, the compère—an attractive man in his forties—kissed her, and with some enthusiasm. For excitement had made her perfectly shaped face even lovelier than usual.

As soon as she returned to her place beside Joe, happily clasping her prize, she realised something was wrong. His face was set into hard lines, his whole body tense. And as she sat down and leaned against him, eager to share her pleasure, he jerked away.

'What is it?' she asked. But he had not answered her then. Instead he stood up and stalked from the room, and an anxious Claire followed him.

In their bedroom he turned on her. 'You enjoyed that, didn't you?' he demanded savagely. 'That—that *gigolo* slobbering all over you! Did you *have* to encourage him like that? Dammit, Claire, you're on your honeymoon, for God's sake. Aren't you getting enough?' And to her horror he had thrown her on to the bed, roughly pulling her clothing aside, and taken her without any gentle loving preliminaries.

'Claire? Whatever's the matter?' Wanda was demanding.

'Sorry, did I disturb you?' She must have groaned aloud. 'I . . . I was just remembering——'

'Well, don't! Put that blasted man out of your mind. You know what that marriage guidance counsellor told you. In no way was any of it your fault.'

Yes, Claire thought, in desperation she had even gone for marriage guidance. Joe had managed to convince her at one point that she was to blame for everything. He had refused to accompany her. 'It's you that needs sorting out,' he'd told her.

That incident on their honeymoon had set the pattern for the months that followed. He'd been apologetic, the morning after that first time. He'd even wept, begged her pardon.

'It's because I love you so much, Claire. I couldn't bear to see that fellow holding you, kissing you. And you seemed to be enjoying it. I was afraid you might enjoy his kisses more than mine. Forgive me?'

And naturally she had forgiven him. Because she'd loved him too she had thought she understood. She shuddered now, realising just how far she had been then from understanding. The last year had taken on the aspect of a nightmare, one she still constantly re-lived, even though it was over.

'Claire, did you hear what I said? Put that man out of your mind and for heaven's sake let's get some sleep. We've got another long drive tomorrow—another load of maniac holiday drivers to face!'

The late July traffic *was* horrendous next day, with twenty-mile tailbacks on the autoroute. Cars and tempers—Wanda's in particular—were becoming overheated. The road was a long mirage, liquid and rippling in the sun's glare. But at last—Provence. A dramatic region, black with cypress, silver with olive trees, the deep dusky red of its soil contrasting shock-ingly with the golden yellow of cornfields. And then—Puit de Mirabeau, close to the foothills of the Luberon Mountains.

Wanda's description of their destination had been a nice piece of understatement, Claire discovered as they drove down the one and only street with its few straggling houses. However, they did not stop in Puit de Mirabeau, but carried on along a road which plunged suddenly into a beautiful wild valley with no sign of human habitation except a couple of farms, well spaced. There was no traffic and no pedestrians. About two miles along this road, Wanda slowed the van and turned off through a gateway into a large field.

'Is this it?' Claire was taken aback. An ordinary field? No facilities? And in a corner one small tent—the only evidence of any other holidaymakers.

'This is it!' Wanda confirmed. 'Right away from it all!'

A puzzled Claire shook her red curls slightly. This was Wanda, the gregarious socialite, the frequenter of publishers' parties, always the centre of the 'in crowd'. It just didn't add up.

'What now?' she asked.

'We have to see the owner—and pay our ground rent.' From her handbag Wanda pulled an envelope containing a thick wad of notes. 'Will you do it, there's a pet? I have a smacking headache from driving into that sun.'

'Now?' Claire asked.

'Of course now!' Wanda sounded irritable—not for the first time in the past three days.

Claire sighed. She too had the beginnings of a headache. She was hot and sticky, and the caravan's shower cabinet was an inviting prospect. But she didn't want to fall out with Wanda at the beginning of their holiday.

'Where do I go?' she asked. Since they had passed the remote farmhouse there had been no other buildings.

'About another mile down the road, apparently.' Wanda consulted a small photostatted map. 'Le Moulin Gris, and ask for Madame Pierrepointe.'

'Is she the owner?'

'I suppose so.' By this time Wanda was lying flat with her eyes closed.

Claire stifled another sigh and extricated her bicycle from among their other luggage. At least the valley terrain seemed to be flat. On her bicycle she could be there and back in no time. She slung her camera over her shoulder—you never knew when an interesting subject might present itself—and set off.

Although it was still oppressively hot, she found she was enjoying the exercise of bicycling after so many hours in the cab of the motor-caravan. The valley seemed to be very sparsely inhabited indeed, lined with low green shrub- and tree-covered hills, full of olive groves and cherry orchards. In no time at all, it seemed, she spotted a discreet sign pointing off to the right—'Le Moulin Gris'.

Her bicycle wheels scrunched noisily over the pebbles of a driveway that seemed to go on for ever, interspersed at intervals by cattle-grids. But at last she rounded a bend—and there it was.

'Oh!' She braked abruptly, which nearly had disastrous consequences. But she saved herself from a fall and stood, lips parted, eyes wide, drinking in the scene before her.

The Moulin Gris was not the ordinary windmill she had expected but an ancient watermill, standing against a backdrop of hills and astride a river where it widened into a deep pool.

It was easy to see where the place had got its name. Blue-grey slate roofs swept steeply down to half-timbered walls, softened by climbing roses, while vast white tubs rioted with cheerful yellow and orange nasturtiums. What a picture it made! Claire patted her camera with a promise of delights to come. But first things first.

The front door was on the first floor, approached by a steep flight of steps.

'Madame Pierrepointe?' Claire enquired of the stout, aproned woman who appeared in answer to her knock.

'*Oui?*'

'We've parked our caravan in your field,' Claire said in French. 'I've come to pay the rent.'

'I speak English good,' the woman informed her. 'I 'ave *mademoiselle's* letter of application,' Madame Pierrepointe rattled on. 'Please to enter.' She stood aside, holding the door invitingly wide, and Claire needed no second invitation. She was dying to see inside.

The entrance to the mill led directly between the living and dining areas, affording tantalising glimpses of these rooms. A marquetry pattern of bricks covered the floor and an antique table held a striking arrangement of flowers in a vast *cloisonné* pot.

'You have a beautiful house,' Claire said as Madame Pierrepoint completed a receipt for Wanda's money. But to her surprise the elderly woman shook her head.

'*Non, mademoiselle*. This is not *my* home, but that of Monsieur Savage. Monsieur Ross Savage?' It was said with pride and she paused, head expectantly on one side, as though anticipating some reaction. But when Claire showed only polite attention, she went on, 'Like yourself, he is English. I am *monsieur's* housekeeper. Only the field where you park, you understand, is mine.'

From Madame Pierrepointe, Claire also learned that eggs, milk and water when necessary could be obtained from the millhouse. 'For all other provisions,' Madame Pierrepointe said, 'it will be necessary to go into Cadenet.' And Claire left with Madame's wishes for a pleasant stay in Puit de Mirabeau.

At the bend in the drive, Claire dismounted from her cycle once more and took her camera from its protective case. She spent some time composing the photograph of the mill itself. If only, she thought wistfully, she could have done some interior shots as well!

Just as she was about to return the camera to its case, a movement on the hill above the mill drew her attention. A man, a horse and a dog. There was a nobility about the grouping that caught her eye—the rich chestnut of the horse, glowing in the sunlight; the erect yet graceful seat of the rider, his blue shirt echoing the colour of the sky; the alert stance of the great dog. It was a sight no dedicated photographer could resist. Claire certainly could not.

Praying that they would not move before she had captured their picture, she slid the telephoto lens to its fullest extent. It was a powerful instrument, powerful enough to bring the rider's features into sharp focus, and so startlingly arresting was his face that for a moment Claire almost forgot the importance of composition. Then, recalling herself, she adjusted the lens, so that not just the face but the trio filled the frame—and took her picture.

Something—perhaps it was the sunlight glinting on the camera—had alerted the rider to her presence. Suddenly he put his mount into motion, galloping along the crest of the ridge, then turning towards her, the dog following and then outstripping the horse.

If they had been magnificent as a static pose, in flowing movement the three were even more so. As they came closer, an ecstatic Claire took shot after shot. How marvellous to ride like that, as though—like the centaur of mythology—the man were part of the horse. She could ride, but not as well as that. It was an expensive taste she had not been much able to indulge.

It was only when they were within hailing distance that she realised all was not well, that for some reason the rider was furiously angry. This, combined with the size of the rapidly advancing dog, panicked her. Slinging the camera strap over her shoulder, she mounted her bicycle, intent on flight.

It had been ridiculous, of course, and if she'd had time for reasoned thought she would have realised she could not possibly outstrip dog or rider. But it was the dog who came up with her first. Normally she was not afraid of dogs—but this one! A great grey shaggy brute he seemed, with large white fangs and an enormous lolling tongue.

She swerved away from the animal and the bicycle's wheels skidded on the loose gravel. As though in slow motion, Claire felt herself toppling, then cycle and rider crashed to the ground in a tangle of wheels and slender bare legs.

As she lay, too winded even to scream, the dog straddled her, his great jaws only inches from her face. Despairingly Claire closed her eyes, flinging up an arm to protect her face from those strong white teeth.

'Wolf! Heel!'

Thank God the brute was obedient. As she sensed the animal's withdrawal, Claire opened her eyes, only to encounter an equally daunting prospect.

The man stood over her, his long legs in riding breeches aggressively astride, his hands on his hips. He was immensely tall, wide-shouldered yet elegantly lean. His dark hair, liberally sprinkled with grey, framed a sun-bronzed but granite-hard face, long-nosed and square-chinned. His grey eyes, as bleak as the rest of him, were hostile.

'What the hell are you up to?' rasped a deeply harsh voice. 'As if I couldn't guess!'

CHAPTER TWO

As Claire stared up at the angry stranger she was possessed by an uneasy sense of familiarity. But that was not possible. She had never met this man before.

Then she realised what it must be. Apart from his height and the grey threading his hair, this might have been Joe standing over her—a similar cast of features, the harsh expression, the fury in the grey eyes. Just so had Joe looked when he'd lost his temper with her, the only difference being that this man had not struck her.

At the memory of Joe's violent, jealous rages, a spasm of remembered fear tremored through her. It must have been evident in her face too, for when the man spoke again it was with impatient scorn.

'For God's sake, woman, I'm not about to molest you! Get up and give an account of yourself.' He extended a hand, but Claire ignored the proffered help.

Her heart was still thudding unpleasantly as, disentangling herself from the bicycle, she attempted to rise, then sank back with a cry of pain. Her ankle, which had been turned at an unnatural angle, had refused to hold her.

With an oath the man squatted beside her. Strong but not ungentle hands straightened the injured leg and fingers probed investigatively.

At his touch Claire felt herself, unaccountably, colouring. She was suddenly uncomfortably aware of the extreme brevity of her holiday shorts and the deep

V of her T-shirt that was revealing far too much of creamy rounded flesh.

'That hurt?' The grey eyes were fixed keenly on her face.

She nodded. 'B-but I'm sure I'll be all right in a minute. If you'll j-just go and leave me alone.' She found herself stammering like a nervous child, unable to meet his penetrating eyes.

'No way!' He drew himself up to his full arrogant height once more. 'I've only your word for it that you *are* in pain. How do I know what else you'll be up to the moment my back's turned?'

'What *else*?' Puzzled green eyes tried to fathom his expression. 'What do you mean? I haven't done anything wrong.' This was Joe all over again, she thought with sick remembrance. Unwarranted accusations.

His mouth twisted in derisive disbelief, just as Joe's would have done. Yes, he was the very type she had vowed to avoid in future.

'For a start, you're trespassing,' he told her. 'Then you were taking photographs of me and my property without permission—which, incidentally, would not have been granted. That's enough to be going on with.' And before she could guess what he was going to do he had seized her camera, flipped it open and removed the film.

'*Oh!*' Claire exclaimed, furious at his high-handed behaviour. 'Those were my holiday photographs you've just ruined!'

'*Holiday photos!*' he sneered. 'That's a good one. But we'll soon find out the truth.'

'The truth?' Claire's temper was rising. Because she'd had to lie to Joe only to protect herself, she had compensated by being scrupulously honest with everyone else. 'Why the hell should I lie to you?'

He did not answer. Instead he bent over her again and scooped her up. Then, bearing her slight weight with ease, he strode towards the house, the great grey dog following.

His strength, the closeness of him, made Claire feel slightly dizzy. But perhaps it was the heat of the Provençal sun—or the shock of her fall. In vain she struggled.

'Put me down, damn you! Where are you taking me?' Then, as it became obvious where they were going, something he had said earlier registered. 'You said this was *your* property? *You're* Mr Savage? Your housekeeper——'

'Oh, surprise, surprise!' he interrupted sarcastically. Then, with deepening anger. 'Don't play the innocent with me. You know damned well who I am. Why else would you be here?'

He was so…so *sure* of himself, Claire seethed. But she would not demean herself to argue further with him. She didn't know who or what he thought she was, but he was in for a salutary lesson very shortly. His housekeeper would quickly confirm the innocence of her presence here.

It was all very well deciding to maintain a dignified silence, but, Claire discovered, it left her no occupation but to become aware of the man who carried her. A very masculine man who—and a shiver passed through her—in different circumstances might have presented her with an immediate sexual challenge. There was that unbidden thrill, the body chemistry.

How fortunate that he had given her instant cause to dislike him! How fortunate that—because of Joe— she was totally immune to his type of man. Her relationship with her former husband had been so much based on physical attraction that she had sworn never to be so swayed again.

His breathing not a whit disturbed by the exertion of carrying her, he mounted the steep stone steps to the door and shouldered it open. Passing through the familiar hallway, he entered the living area which— only a short while ago—she had longed to see in detail.

It was as spectacular as she had suspected, some nine or ten metres high with full-height windows looking out towards the range of hills. Above her open galleries led, presumably, to bedrooms.

He deposited her on one of two long, cream-upholstered couches and thrust a bright yellow cushion beneath her head.

'Stay there!' he instructed unnecessarily. Much as she longed to escape, Claire knew her ankle was not yet equal to the attempt. Besides, the dog, as though receiving some telepathic message from his master, was between her and the door, watching her with large intelligent eyes.

As Ross Savage disappeared with long, pantherish strides into some other region of the house, she looked about her. Might as well make the most of the opportunity, she thought philosophically.

Without destroying its essential character, the old millhouse had been made into a strikingly different home, its restoration and conversion involving much sympathetic use of old stone and brickwork.

Glass had been inserted between some of the vertical timbers, to provide windows, and rough "dragged" paintwork coated the internal walls. The furnishings were almost stark in their severe simplicity—a fit setting for a man who, by his taste, she suspected despised the frills of life.

She was not allowed long for her inspection.

'I've telephoned for the doctor,' Ross Savage announced as he returned, 'so we'll soon know if you're faking that ankle injury.'

'I suppose,' Claire said with heavy irony, 'you didn't happen to ask Madame Pierrepointe——'

'You people do your homework, don't you?' But it was not an expression of admiration. 'You even know the name of my housekeeper. Perhaps you can also tell me where I buy my shirts and underclothes? Incidentally, which filthy rag are *you* with?'

Green eyes puzzled now, Claire stared at him. 'I don't——'

'For heaven's sake, spare me the wide-eyed innocence! I suppose they thought I'd be more susceptible to a beautiful woman.' He gave a cynical laugh. 'They couldn't have been more wrong!'

Despite his disclaimer, there was something in the grey eyes which told Claire he really did find her attractive. But 'beautiful'? She had certainly never thought of herself in those terms. To her, beauty was something strikingly different, unusual, not her own unexcitingly regular features, framed by molten copper curls. Now, if she had been a statuesque, blue-eyed blonde or a sultry brunette...

'You haven't answered my question.' Impatiently he broke in on her train of thought. 'What newspaper or magazine are you with?'

Light dawned. 'I'm not a journalist!' a relieved Claire exclaimed. 'Whatever gave you that extraordinary idea? And even supposing I were,' she added witheringly, 'why would I be interested in *you*? I've never heard of you.'

For a moment there was uncertainty in the grey eyes studying her. Then he shook his head. 'You'd be bound to say that. But I'm not so easily fooled.

I——' He broke off, his head cocked in a listening attitude. Claire too had heard the crunch of wheels on gravel. 'That will be Dr Leclerc. He's retired from general practice, but he's still very much on the ball. So if you're faking...' He left the outcome to her imagination.

Dr Leclerc was a small ball of a man, with keen dark eyes behind his pince-nez. His hands were soft and gentle on the swollen joint. He pronounced the ankle to be not sprained but certainly badly strained.

Claire groaned. 'How long before I can walk on it? I'm on holiday, and I was looking forward to some sightseeing.'

'A week, ten days, maybe. I'm sorry, *mademoiselle*, but I am afraid your sightseeing is going to be sadly limited. It might be as well to cut your losses and go home.'

Claire smiled wryly. 'At the moment my "home" is parked in a field further down the road, and——'

'You're parked in that field?' Ross Savage exploded. 'Well, of all the nerve!'

Claire stared at him. It was a camping site, wasn't it? So why the indignation? 'My cousin and I...' she began, then, 'Heavens—Wanda! My cousin will be wondering where on earth I've got to!'

'Your *cousin*?' Ross Savage echoed, a wealth of scepticism in his voice. 'You're sure you don't mean colleague?' And, as if some light had suddenly dawned, 'I get it, you're the photographer, *she's* the journalist!'

It was too much. Claire exploded. 'Now look here, you... you high-handed, disbelieving, overbearing...' She bit back the unpleasant epithet she had been tempted to use. Wanda would have used it unhesitatingly, but a year of Joe's bad language had made Claire determined never to use anything more than the mildest expletive.

She took a deep breath and began again, more calmly, 'Just get it through your thick skull, will you? I am *not* a journalist, and Wanda——' She stopped abruptly. Because Wanda *was* a journalist. 'Wanda *is* my cousin,' she finished lamely.

'Hmm.' Ross Savage still sounded unconvinced. 'I'll just see the good doctor out and then we'll get you back to your caravan—and your cousin. I'd like to look her over for myself.'

Oh, heavens, Claire thought as the two men left the room. Suppose Ross Savage recognised Wanda? He had to know a lot about journalists to be so opposed to them; and if—as seemed likely—he *was* famous he could well have encountered her cousin at some time.

So what if he *did* know Wanda? she asked herself bracingly. But she knew the answer to that one. He would take it as proof that she had lied to him. She must keep him away from the caravan until she'd had a chance to brief Wanda, to ask her if she knew Ross Savage. So the moment he walked back through the door she broke into speech.

'There's really no need for you to bother any more about me. I'm sure my ankle won't stop me riding my bicycle. I——'

'Maybe your ankle wouldn't stop you—I don't know. But one thing is certain, you won't be riding your bicycle for a while—the wheel is out of true and you have a flat tyre. I——'

'Monsieur Savage, I am so sorry!' At that moment Madame Pierrepointe bustled into the room. 'I 'ad no idea you 'ad a visitor. I am mortified. I . . . Why, it is the young English lady, Mademoiselle Lovejoy, who rents my parking place for her caravan. Is every-thing——?'

'Hold on! Hold on! *Un moment, madame, s'il vous plaît.*' Ross Savage raised an admonitory hand, stemming the Frenchwoman's rapid flow of speech. 'You say *this* is Miss Lovejoy? You *know* her?'

'*Mais oui, monsieur, bien sûr.* She wrote to me, do you not recall? Me, I showed you the letter—in which she ask for permission to use the field.'

'I did?' said Claire, then hastily changing her emphasis, 'Yes, I did.' It must have been Wanda who had written.

But why on earth, she puzzled, had Wanda signed herself Claire Lovejoy? Again with sickening certainty the answer followed swiftly upon the question—because Wanda knew the set-up at Le Moulin Gris and she dared not use her own name. Therefore...therefore Wanda Hedley and Ross Savage must be known to each other.

Perhaps Bella, the self-styled palmist, hadn't been so far out in her reading of Wanda's hand, Claire thought wryly.

'It seems, Miss Lovejoy,' Ross Savage said slowly, 'that I owe you an apology.' And before Claire could say anything, '*Madame*, do you think we might have afternoon tea? *Mademoiselle* has injured her ankle, owing to my stupidity. The least I can do is refresh her before I return her to her caravan. And, *madame*, please ask Monsieur Pierrepointe to go to the field with a message for *mademoiselle*'s cousin.'

It was unbelievable, the change in his manner.

'Oh, please,' Claire began. 'I don't want to cause any——'

'No trouble at all,' Ross Savage said smoothly as his housekeeper bustled away. He moved to sit beside

Claire and to her amazement he reached out and took her hand in his. 'Will you accept my apology, Miss Lovejoy? I really am extremely sorry. My only excuse is that the field belongs to the Pierrepointes, and though—for reasons I won't go into—*madame* consults me about the lettings...' He shrugged and for the first time Claire saw him smile, his teeth incredibly white against sun-bronzed skin.

The effect of his smile was extraordinary. It was not just a movement of his mouth. Slow, lopsided, charming and entirely captivating, it altered his whole face, transforming him from a brooding aggressor into a disruptively attractive man.

But Claire was not so easily disarmed. Joe had used to smile at her like that, before... Before he'd shown himself in his true colours. She wasn't about to be dazzled by a man's smile again.

So why then were these strange shock waves passing through her? Then she realised he was still holding her hand in a firm clasp, and it seemed to be that which was having this odd effect on her. She snatched her hand away, but it was too late. That male magnetism had already worked its spell. Her hand might be free, but her eyes were still locked with his and she felt the pull of a dynamic personality hitherto only suspected and hidden until now by his cloak of antagonism.

Her mouth was dry, her lips oddly stiff and reluctant to do her bidding. 'Mr Savage,' she croaked, 'I...really ought to be going. My cousin——'

'Gaston Pierrepointe is on his way at this moment to reassure your cousin, and you must allow me to alleviate the guilt I feel at causing your accident.' He turned slightly and clicked his fingers at the dog. 'Here, Wolf!' And as the animal approached, 'Wolf may look alarming, Miss Lovejoy, and in that he serves a purpose—to deter unwanted visitors. But there's no malice in him. See?' Again he took her hand and placed it on the dog's head.

'I'm not normally afraid of dogs, or indeed any animal,' Claire explained as she caressed the beast's shaggy coat, rewarded by a lick from the enormous tongue. 'I love dogs *and* horses. But Wolf is rather large and——'

'And *you* are rather small!' Ross Savage finished for her, but it was said in such a way as to make Claire feel that being of a diminutive stature was the most desirable thing in the world. And Ross Savage's next words confirmed that impression. 'I've always preferred petite, daintily made women. You're quietly spoken too—except . . .' and again that devastating, knee-weakening smile creased his face '. . . except when you're angry. I like that too. I can't abide these great leggy hoydenish women, strident feminists who insist on thrusting their opinions down everyone's throats.'

Immediately Claire had a vision of Wanda. For the daughters of twin sisters she and her cousin were totally unalike. Claire took after her late mother, Wanda resembled her father. But from whom had Wanda inherited her character? That was a puzzle.

'Tell me about yourself, Miss Lovejoy; your tastes, your interests,'

'Oh, but you can't possibly be——'

'Oh, but I *am*. You see, Miss Lovejoy, not only do I feel I owe it to you to restore you with afternoon tea, I also feel I must do something to remedy the ruin of your holiday.'

From beneath delicately arched brows, darker than her hair, Claire looked at him questioningly. 'I don't see how——' she began.

'Then let me explain. But here's the tea.'

And the next few moments were spent in ascertaining her preferences as to milk and sugar. Mouthwateringly light scones were pressed upon her, while Ross Savage handled the china as deftly as any woman—china which, Claire was stunned to note, was of the most delicate porcelain. Surely only a very rich man would *use* china which she would have expected to see displayed in the safety of a glass cabinet?

Claire had hoped the interruption would divert his thoughts from her affairs, but not so. 'Now, to return to the subject of your holiday. You mentioned sightseeing. What did you have in mind?'

'Quite honestly, I don't know,' Claire confessed. 'I know practically nothing about Provence. It's my cousin's holiday really. I just came along on the spur of the moment.'

'Presumably your bicycle was intended for transport?'

'Yes. We thought it would save petrol.' A frown formed between Claire's green eyes. 'Is there anywhere locally I could get it fixed?'

'My blacksmith shall attend to it,' Ross Savage promised. And at her enquiring look, 'Since I own a considerable number of horses, a blacksmith is a useful, even a necessary asset. And aside from attending to my horses he's skilled in other forms of metalwork. Your ankle,' he went on, 'will make cycling an impossibility. Can you ride?'

Claire's eyes widened in startled surmise. Surely he couldn't mean...? Oh, how marvellous that would be, to see this countryside on horseback!

Ross Savage watched in some amusement the play of expression across her small face, the widening of incredibly large green eyes, the sudden flush of ex-

citement in cheeks too pale for this time of year—a
pallor that was not exactly that due to lack of fresh
air. It was almost as if she had been ill. But as he
watched, her face fell, a change that would have been
comical if it had not been for the very real disappointment in those magnificent eyes.

'I can ride,' she said. 'But Wanda can't.'

'And do you intend to spend the entire holiday in
each other's pockets?'

They hadn't intended to do so, Claire thought. But
she had assumed, since Wanda had asked for her
company, that they would spend some of their time
together.

'In view of your injury, your cousin's activities
would be somewhat limited,' Ross Savage pointed out.
'Whereas, if you took advantage of my offer, she
would be free to——'

'It's very kind of you,' Claire said a little breathlessly. It was tempting and he seemed so eager to press
his services on her—unnecessarily eager, surely? Despite the mishap to her bicycle and the injury to her
ankle he had no real obligation towards her.
'But . . . but I really don't think . . . I mean, I'm a
complete stranger to you, and really there's no
need——'

'Suppose we put it to your cousin?' he suggested
good-humouredly. 'At least postpone your decision
until then, hmm? Now, suppose you finish your tea
while I bring my car round to the front.'

Claire shrugged helplessly as she watched his retreating figure. She had the sensation of having been
taken over by an irresistible force. And somehow, she
had to admit, she did not *feel* like resisting. It was
the prospect of riding again, she assured herself, which
was so alluring, not that of Ross Savage's company.

Though—and she couldn't help the thought—his might be preferable to Wanda's.

Immediately she berated herself for disloyalty. But there was no escaping the fact—the last few days with Wanda had reminded her of the side to her cousin's nature that she did not much like. In London Wanda's visits, her support in court, had been very welcome—but then Claire had not had to spend twenty-four hours a day with her.

Wanda had an abrasive manner, an irritable temper and—it would be unrealistic to deny—a hard streak of selfishness. And as for the way she had castigated the French during their drive down through the country——! In fact, Claire was beginning to wonder more and more just why Wanda had chosen France—and Provence in particular—for her holiday.

'Ready?' Despite the intense heat Ross Savage seemed imbued with indefatigable energy. Without giving warning of his intentions he swooped and swung her up into his arms. As he did so, his hand accidentally brushed against her breast, and her heart began that ridiculously wild thumping again.

'Mr Savage!' Claire protested, colour staining her cheeks once more—not with excitement this time but with this repetition of her uncomfortable awareness of him. 'I'm sure I could walk as far as your car.'

'Let's not take any chances, eh? If you were an Amazon,' he said with another of those attractive, lopsided grins, 'I might not be so gallant. But you're just a featherweight in my arms.'

Somehow that expression ''in my arms'', following upon that brief but disturbing contact, seemed to imply a deeper intimacy, and Claire's heart skipped an erratic beat.

For heaven's sake, she scolded herself, don't go reading more into this situation than it warrants. You met this man an hour ago and you probably won't see him again. Wanda isn't going to blithely agree to your swanning off with him and leaving her to her own devices. In fact it's more likely she'll set her own sights on him. He's just the sort she'd go for—stunningly handsome, rich ... But Claire found this prediction did not please her at all.

'My car!' His voice broke across this unaccountable feeling of dismay. 'Put your arms round my neck and I'll lower you in.'

The vehicle, a modest standard Citroën 2CV, was not at all the kind of car she would have expected Ross Savage to own. But for the moment she was more concerned with his order. She felt a strange panicky reluctance to put her arms around that strongly corded neck with its coating of thick virile hair. But it was obvious he didn't intend to put her down until she complied.

Unaware that she did so, Claire took a deep breath and closed her eyes. Gingerly she placed her fingertips around the back of his neck and at once experienced the sensation she had expected, and feared— a powerful *frisson* that seemed to travel the length of her arms and descend rapidly through her body, invading a region that she was shocked to find affected by him. A shuddering little sigh racked her as carefully he lowered her into the Citroën's passenger-seat. Fortunately he mistook it for a gasp of pain.

'Sorry. Damned awkward—not the ideal carriage for a "maiden in distress", is it? It might have been better to take you up on my horse.'

But that would have involved being close to him for a much longer period.

'No, this is fine, really,' she assured him, her poise returning now that there was no physical contact between them.

No physical contact, and yet she was very aware of him as they drove away from the mill, and irresistibly her eyes were drawn to the large capable hands on the steering-wheel—large and capable, yes, but with unusually long fingers, their nails well tended. Nice hands. Nice to touch. And the thought brought another of those shamingly physical symptoms. Deliberately she averted her eyes.

It took far less time to reach the caravan site than it had taken Claire for the reverse route on her bicycle. Halfway there, Ross Savage slowed the car to speak to a giant of a man in old blue trousers and frayed, faded shirt, making his unhurried way towards them. Ross spoke in French, but Claire understood.

'Gaston, you delivered the message?'

Gaston's wedge of a nose jutted out above a ragged nicotine-stained moustache which made his reply, in a strong local accent, a little more difficult to follow, but Claire gathered that he had seen Wanda and assured her of her cousin's safety in the house of Monsieur Savage and that Monsieur Savage himself would be returning Claire to the camping site.

As the Citroën jolted slowly across the rutted field, Ross Savage patted its dashboard with an affectionate hand. 'The old girl's just the job for this kind of terrain—surprisingly resilient springs. It's a model that hasn't changed much in the last twenty-five years, consequently spare parts are available all over France. Which is why I hang on to her instead of investing in something more up-to-date.'

'I did wonder,' Claire confessed. 'It didn't seem to fit your image somehow.'

The car came to an abrupt halt. 'My image?' It was said sharply, with a return to the suspicious hostility he had evinced earlier. 'What exactly do you mean by that? What image?'

She turned puzzled eyes towards him. Why *was* he so defensive? *Ought* she to have heard of him?

'I only meant that what I've seen of you so far— your home, your lifestyle . . . Well, I mean, you're not *poor*, are you?'

'So?' There was still a piercing glitter in the grey eyes.

'So nothing!' she said exasperatedly. 'That's all. What else did you think I meant?'

He went on regarding her for a long instant. Then he seemed to relax. He shrugged broad shoulders and put the Citroën into low gear once more. 'Nothing. Maybe,' he said cryptically.

They did not speak again until they reached the motor-caravan, standing in the corner of the field. Claire was beginning to feel decidedly apprehensive about the coming encounter with Wanda. If Ross Savage should recognise her for who and what she was . . . Well, that would be the end of everything. She would not allow herself to examine the full extent of what she meant by 'everything'. But almost certainly it would mean their ignominious eviction from Puit de Mirabeau.

As Ross got out of the car, Claire opened the passenger door, slid from the seat and was on her feet before he could reach her. She didn't *want* him to touch her again, to lift her. But the reward for her pains was a complete disregard for her wishes—and a scolding.

'Little fool! Do you want to set your recovery back?' And once again she knew that disconcerting nearness, the pungent aroma of cologne overlying that other less tangible, indefinable musky maleness.

There was no response to his knock on the door of the van, but it was not locked. He strode in and deposited Claire on one of the bunks. She looked about her. There was no sign of Wanda—nor of her cousin's bicycle.

'She must have decided to cycle back to the village for something,' Claire excused hastily, quite forgetting that Puit de Mirabeau had not boasted any shops.

'I can't think what for,' Ross said drily. 'But she obviously wasn't concerned enough for your injury to await your return.' He hesitated. 'Will you be all right? Or would you like me to stay until she comes, back?'

In the confined space of the motor-caravan he seemed even larger and more formidable than in his own home. And there at least there had been the reassuring if invisible presence of Madame Pierrepointe. Here they were quite alone. Not that there was any logical reason to fear being alone with him, Claire told herself, but suddenly she was anxious to be rid of him.

'I'll be quite all right,' she said. 'I'm sure Wanda won't be long. She was too tired to have gone far.'

From behind the curtains she watched him get back into his car and drive off, and not till the Citroën reached the road and turned out of sight did she quite relax.

She had leisure now to think what Wanda's disappearance really meant, for her quick excuse had been for Ross Savage's benefit. Gaston Pierrepointe had delivered Ross's message. And it seemed the intelligence that Ross himself intended to visit the caravan had driven an exhausted Wanda to flight. Claire was willing to bet that her cousin was not far away—concealed somewhere out of sight, no doubt, until Ross had left.

Sure enough, it was only a few moments before she heard the bicycle and Wanda entered the van.

'How's the ankle?' Wanda asked, and Claire knew very well that the question was meant merely to stave off the more awkward enquiries Claire planned.

'Painful,' she said. Then bluntly, 'Just what are you up to, Wanda? Why did you scoot off like that? Something's up, isn't it? Do you and Ross Savage know each other?'

Either Wanda was telling the truth or she had prepared herself well, for her pale blue eyes held Claire's hardily. 'Never met him, never even heard of him.'

'Then why avoid him?'

'For the same reason I'd avoid anyone else. This is a holiday; I want to get away from people. And I certainly don't want to socialise with the locals.'

Claire looked at her doubtfully. *Was* she misjudging Wanda? 'He's not French, actually. He's English.'

'Oh?' Wanda shrugged indifferently. 'It must be the way that brutish peasant type pronounced his name. I thought he said "Sauvage". Anyway, you'd better tell me about your little adventure. What happened, exactly? I only understood one word in ten of the peasant's story.'

Launched into her story, the description of the Moulin Gris, its architecture and interior, and not least of all its owner, Claire did not realise just how enthusiastic and revealing a picture she was painting, until Wanda's high-pitched laugh rang out.

'Taken quite a fancy to this Ross Savage, haven't you? Careful, coz! Remember the palmist's warning! Recent divorcees are very vulnerable—love on the re-bound and all that!'

'Rubbish!' Claire said crossly. But afterwards she wondered if she would have been so annoyed if there had not been some truth in Wanda's words. It was all very well to declare that once bitten was twice shy; that she did not intend to get involved with another man for a very long time, if ever. But there was no accounting for the chemistry of attraction. Still, that was all it had been, she reassured herself. You could recognise a man's physical attributes without necess-arily wanting to take advantage of them. And be-sides, there was that fleeting resemblance to Joe. She shivered.

'Do you intend to take him up on his offer of a horse?' asked Wanda.

Claire shook her head. 'I couldn't, could I? For one thing, he was probably only being polite—be-cause he felt my accident was partly his fault. And for another, it wouldn't be fair to you.'

Wanda laughed again. 'Good lord, Claire, don't let *me* stop you! You'll hardly be able to keep up with me now, will you? And I certainly don't intend to hang around this benighted field and village for the next three weeks. Just because I told you to be careful it doesn't mean you shouldn't snap up the chance to cultivate this Mr Savage. It looks as though Bella's predictions could be right. And a little holiday ro-mance might be just the thing to snap you out of that slough of despond you've been in.'

'I don't *want* a holiday romance, thanks,' Claire said positively. 'But I must admit the chance to ride... Wanda, I... Are you sure?'

'Of course I'm sure.' Wanda sounded more cheerful than she had for days. 'I'll do my thing and you do yours, and we'll swap yarns at the end of each day, yes? You never know, it might be more fun in the end. All I ask is, don't inflict him on me!'

Which was all very well, Claire thought next morning, after an unnaturally cheerful Wanda had left, very early, on her bicycle. Her cousin had declared her intention of being gone all day. But for the fact that Wanda had never been to Provence before, Claire might have suspected her cousin of having a secret assignation.

But it didn't have to be with a Frenchman, she realised suddenly. It could be Wanda's latest boy-friend—in all probability another married man who had told his wife some cock-and-bull story about a business trip, but had in fact arranged to meet Wanda in Provence.

And what part had she, Claire, been supposed to play? Wanda's cover, in case awkward questions were asked? For, despite her cousin's predilection for married men, Claire knew that Wanda had no intention of being cited as the 'other woman' in a divorce case.

'Good God!' she'd told Claire once, when questioned about the depth of her feelings for one of these men, 'I wouldn't want any of them permanently. No, when I get bored with them I just send them safely home to Momma.'

Claire felt aggrieved at the idea of being made use of in this way. Still, it was partly her own fault. She had declared her gratitude to Wanda and had virtually given her *carte blanche* to seek favours in return. At least, she thought thankfully, her mishap meant she need not actually meet Wanda's lover—not to mention the inevitable "friend" he would have provided for *her*.

She looked at her watch. Only half an hour had passed since Wanda had left, in which time Claire had washed up their breakfast things, made up the bunks and generally tidied around. What was she to do with the rest of her day? Wanda had blithely assumed that Ross Savage would be back today. But would he? Even if he'd been sincere in his offer, he might leave it a day or two before enquiring.

Although it was early the sun was already warm. Later it would be too hot for sunbathing. She might as well seize *this* opportunity at least. Thank heaven her ankle, though still painful, was no longer swollen. She could just about hobble.

She donned a bright red T-shirt, its neckline cut low and square, and added a floral wrap-around sarong skirt. With a lightweight sunlounger arranged to her satisfaction, she anointed her creamy pale skin with sun-cream, adjusted her hat and sunglasses and settled herself down.

She had still not recovered from the anxious sleepless nights of the past few weeks, the journey to Provence had added its burden of fatigue and the bunk beds were taking a little getting used to. Within minutes Claire was asleep and dreaming.

She was cocooned in soft sensuous warmth—the warmth of a man's arms, a strong but gentle man, tall and bronzed with greying dark hair that grew a little too long and luxuriantly at the nape of his neck, the nape around which her hands were clasped. He had just the sort of male good looks she had always preferred. He was like Joe—and yet he was not like Joe.

Warm sensuality stirred her body and she shifted voluptuously in her chair, disturbing the shady straw hat, which fell to the ground. The sarong skirt fell apart, leaving her shapely legs exposed to the top of her thighs.

The sun crept higher. And higher. It grew hotter.

She was awoken suddenly by a strong, ungentle hand on her shoulder.

'You little idiot! Are you trying to add sunburn to your injuries?'

Still half asleep, still half in that sun-warmed world where this man was her lover, Claire regarded him through glazed green eyes.

'Ross!' she murmured his name huskily and with patent pleasure. A little smile curled her lips, the bottom one pouting slightly in unconscious invitation.

'For Pete's sake! You're frying!' he declared unromantically. 'Good thing I stopped by. Another half-hour and you'd look even more like a boiled lobster. I seem to be making a habit of this,' he added with a trace of irritation as he yanked her from the lounger and carried her into the van.

Wide awake now and horribly embarrassed by the vivid dream that for a moment had followed her into reality, Claire struggled and protested vigorously.

'Put me down! You're not my minder!' Because of those few seconds when she had regarded him with all the soft satisfaction of an accepted lover, she was sharper in her tone than she might have been.

'Someone ought to be!' he retorted. 'Where's that cousin of yours?' He looked about the caravan as if expecting Wanda to suddenly materialise.

'Gone out for the day.'

'And left you all alone! Damned irresponsible——'

'Don't blame Wanda!' Claire interrupted. 'I told her I didn't mind. I told her about your offer to take me riding and she——'

'My *what*?' He had been pacing the small confines of the van. Now he came to an abrupt stop. 'My what?' he repeated.

Puzzled by his brusqueness, she stared up at him. 'You asked me if I could ride and——'

'I offered to lend you a horse, yes—and I would have sent one of my stable lads.' Sarcastically, 'I wasn't aware that I'd offered any personal service.'

'Oh!' Claire didn't know whether she was more disappointed or embarrassed. But whatever it was, she felt furiously angry, though whether it was with him or with herself she wasn't sure. 'Obviously I misunderstood,' she said stiffly, and turned her head away so he would not see the stupid tears which had sprung to her eyes. She had cried too easily of late. She wished he would go away.

Disconcertingly, Ross sat down on the edge of the bunk bed. A large hand shot out and captured her chin, inexorably turning her face towards him. He saw the tears.

'Hey,' he said softly, 'did it mean *that* much to you?' Then, grimly, 'Why, I wonder?'

He must never guess at the foolish reason—foolish because she didn't want to feel this compelling attraction he seemed to exude. She needed another man in her life the way she needed a hole in the head.

Indeed, Claire was beginning to think she must *have* a hole in her skull through which any brains she possessed had seeped out.

'I couldn't care less!' she said sharply, jerking her chin from his grasp. 'I misunderstood, that's all, and I feel stupid. I thought you'd made a generous offer and I didn't want to seem rude and ungrateful. As it happens, I'm quite glad I *was* wrong. I came here for a rest—to get away from things and . . . and people . . . away from . . .' She broke off.

'From men in particular?' he guessed shrewdly.

She stared at him in surprise. 'What makes you say that?'

He shrugged. 'Your whole manner towards me. You don't enjoy being touched, do you? Every time I've lifted you, you tremble, and I've sensed this shrinking away. When we first met you looked as though you thought I was going to physically assault you. You've had some of that, haven't you,' he went on, 'physical violence?'

Her eyes shadowed, she nodded.

'He must have been a mad brute!' There was anger in Ross Savage's voice now. 'You're so small, so vulnerable-looking.' He reached out and picked up her left hand, where the mark of a wedding-ring was still visible. 'You've been married, haven't you? It *was* your husband?' he asked.

Again Claire nodded and her lips quivered. She'd thought to put all that behind her, but it was still too recent, and Ross's questioning was resurrecting those dreadful memories and the sympathy in his voice had brought the all-too-ready tears to her eyes once more.

He retained her hand, his forefinger gently rubbing the mark where the ring had been, as though he would erase it. 'Not all men are brutes,' he said. And then roughly, as he looked into her tear-filled eyes, 'For God's sake, woman, don't cry! The only way I've ever discovered to stop a woman crying once she starts is to kiss her. And I'm tired of kissing.'

CHAPTER THREE

'WHAT a strange thing to say!' Diverted, Claire searched Ross's face for some explanation.

'Strange?' His voice was harsh. 'To you, yes, maybe. But you're a woman and I suppose much like all the rest. Believe me, I've kissed enough women to last me a lifetime.'

And he sounded as though he really meant it. Claire stared at him in wonderment which gradually turned to scorn. He must be the worst kind of philanderer! So sexually experienced that he had even sickened himself by his excesses. She snatched her hand away in a gesture of revulsion.

'Well, you needn't worry,' she said coldly. 'I'm certainly not expecting you to kiss *me*. In fact that's the very last thing I'd want!'

At her vehemence he looked a little taken aback, but when he spoke it was with evident relief. 'Good. Well, now that we've got that clear we *both* know how to proceed.'

'How to proceed?' she echoed.

'As chance acquaintances—strangers thrown together.' Suddenly he smiled. 'Friendly strangers, I hope—but nothing more. Agreed?'

Claire wavered indecisively. It was silly, illogical, but she had the most alarming presentiment of danger. Maybe she ought not to have anything to do with this man at all. Maybe she should refuse his invitation.

But in spite of this, 'Agreed,' she said faintly. 'But . . . but we don't even have to be that, if you'd prefer not to. I've told you before, you need have no sense of obligation towards me. I——'

'But I have,' he said firmly, 'and, that established—and since we've agreed to be friends—isn't it about time I knew your name? Other than Miss Lovejoy, I mean. I'm Ross—as you may have already gathered?'

'Claire,' she told him.

'Claire it is. And now, suppose I take you back to my place for morning coffee and then we'll sort out a suitable mount for you. How much experience have you of riding?'

'Quite a bit—before I was married. But I haven't ridden in over a year.' Horse-riding had been another interest denied her, since Joe couldn't share it. He'd been nervous of anything larger than a dog.

'It's not something you forget how to do,' Ross assured her. 'Though you'd better not overdo it to start with.' Then, 'What's wrong?' For her face had fallen.

'I've just realised—I can't go riding. I've no suitable clothes with me. I can hardly ride in shorts or skirts.'

'No problem! I can kit you out.'

Her transportation to Ross's car was effected once again, in the customary manner. But this time Claire was ready for it and steeled herself to accept his touch as impersonally as it was bestowed. If he was off women, she was just as certainly off men, she reminded herself. Even though she was disillusioned where he, obviously, was merely sated.

Even though she had last entered it under such different circumstances, there was a welcoming sense of familiarity about the Moulin Gris. Almost a sense of homecoming. It *would* be a delightful place to live, she thought, relaxing into the cushioned comfort of its modern furnishings.

'You have a lovely house,' she told Ross, as once she had, mistakenly, told Madame Pierrepointe.

He seemed pleased. 'I think so too. Would you like to see the rest of it?'

'Yes, I'd love to, but...' she added hastily, 'when my ankle is better and I can walk. I can't expect you to go lugging me all over the place.'

The grey eyes twinkled. They could be so disarming, Claire thought involuntarily, when he wasn't angry about something. 'I'd hardly describe carrying you as "lugging"! As I said before, there's nothing of you. That's your build, of course.' His eyes were frankly assessing. 'But at a guess I'd say you were also underweight. Due to recent events? Your unhappy marriage, possibly?'

'Yes. But please, I don't want to talk about it. Couldn't we...couldn't we talk about you instead?'

For a moment she saw that old wariness in his eyes. Surely he didn't still distrust her? Then, 'OK. What do you want to know?'

She was full of curiosity about Ross Savage, she realised, despite her dislike of the womanising character he had projected. But where to start, without making him shy away again like one of his horses? Horses—yes, that surely was a safe subject.

'Tell me about your stable. Do you breed? Race them, maybe? And how,' daringly, 'does an Englishman come to be doing this in the middle of France?'

She'd dared too much. There was a repetition of his closed-in expression. 'We'll leave out your third question, if you don't mind. As to the first two—yes, I both breed and race. Or rather, I have a trainer and

stable lads who do it for me. *My* main occupation
these days is my writing.'

'Writing?' Despite her love of riding Claire knew
little or nothing about breeding horses. But, through
Wanda, she did know quite a bit about writing. 'That's
interesting. What sort of things do you write? Do you
use your own name?' And, apologetically, 'Is *that* why
I ought to have heard of you?'

He laughed aloud, an attractive sound. 'Do you
always ask your questions in threes? I write adventure
yarns, chiefly based on my own mad exploits. Yes, I
use my own name. And no, unless you read my sort
of book you wouldn't have heard of me.'

'Your own mad exploits?' In her interest Claire had
quite forgotten her mistrust of him, her distaste for
his declared womanising. 'Now I *am* intrigued. *What*
exploits?'

He seemed very relaxed now, seated beside her, long
legs stretched out in front of him, one arm flung along
the back of the couch, and though she was aware of
it, only inches from her shoulders, Claire steadfastly
kept her mind on what he was saying.

'I've tried just about everything. I won't write about
it unless I've done it. Mountain climbing, pot-holing,
shooting the rapids in canoes, abseiling, hang-gliding,
micro-light flying. My current obsession is hot-air-
ballooning.'

Claire's green eyes shone. 'Oh,' she said wistfully,
'you are lucky to be able to afford to try all those
things—the sort of things most people only dream of.'

He seemed amused by her fervour. 'Do you mean
to tell me that kind of thing appeals to you?' And as
she nodded, 'Well, I'm blessed! That little body of
yours looks too frail to contain such an adventurous
spirit.'

At his comprehensive survey, Claire blushed. But, 'Tell me about some of it,' she begged, and then repentantly, as he glanced at his watch, 'Oh, I'm sorry, you're probably too busy. I know writers like to keep to a schedule. I mustn't waste any more of your time.' She put down her empty coffee cup and, forgetting her injury, sprang to her feet, only to have her ankle give under her.

With a little cry of mingled pain and irritation at her own stupid forgetfulness, she crumpled into strong arms that shot out and deftly fielded her.

'Little idiot!' Ross growled in his throat as, for a brief instant, she rested against his broad chest—a brief instant, but long enough to hear the rapid thudding of his heart and to send the blood rushing up once more into her own face. 'Don't be in such a hurry,' he said as he lifted her. 'It's not that I haven't the time—or the inclination—to tell you about these things. I have. But because of the heat at this time of year, between midday and evening strenuous activity is out of the question. So if we're to get any riding in this morning——'

'We?' she queried, so far forgetting her flushed cheeks as to peer up into his face. 'But I thought——'

'So did I,' he said grimly. 'But I've changed my mind. I've decided to make myself personally responsible for your safety.'

Why? she wondered with pounding pulses as he carried her out of the house, round the side and into the stable yard. Why the change of heart? No, change of mind, she corrected herself. Ross Savage's heart— if he even had one—had nothing to do with it, or with her.

The stable yard, as if she had needed any proof of it, bore all the evidence of his wealth. Pristine white paintwork, weed-free gravel, a central island of closely manicured turf, handsome, intelligent thoroughbreds looking out over the half-doors of the loose-boxes, and a bevy of men going briskly about their tasks.

Ross spoke rapidly to one of the deferential stable lads and within minutes two horses were being saddled and bridled.

Meanwhile, from a deep cupboard in the trainer's office, various articles of riding clothes were produced for Claire's inspection and approval.

'I'll leave you to try them on,' Ross said. 'Unless...' He hesitated. 'Will you need any help—with the breeches—your ankle...?'

At the very notion of Ross's helping her to dress, Claire quivered. 'I can manage,' she told him hastily.

Thank goodness her ankle wasn't still swollen, she thought as she manoeuvred herself into the breeches and pulled on the soft leather boots. She found herself wondering how he came to have such a selection of women's clothes available, then shied away from the thought.

'Ready?' She had donned the shirt but had not fastened the buttons when a brief knock heralded Ross's immediate appearance. For a brief second his eyes rested intently on the small high breasts in their flimsy lace support, and Claire saw a dull flush of colour tinge his brown cheeks. Then he averted his head as if the sight offended him. 'Sorry,' he muttered.

Claire's fingers trembled as they completed their task. 'I'm ready now,' she said with more composure than she felt.

Despite this man's denials of any personal interest in her, deep down she still felt uneasy. Perhaps it *was* just that little something about him which reminded her of Joe. She might even be misjudging the man, of course, but that likeness, however superficial, was nonetheless disturbing. Disturbing because the attraction was there without the repelling violence. For despite his many displays of anger, Claire did not believe Ross Savage would ever strike a woman.

No, that inner voice of doubt said, but he obviously misuses them in other ways.

The mount Ross had selected for her was a gentle mare—Minou.

'She's not one of my racing stock,' he explained, 'but a hack I keep for visitors.'

Female visitors? Claire found herself wondering with a disagreeable little stab of a pique she had no right or desire to feel.

Ross himself was riding Le Carpentier, the same powerful chestnut as yesterday. They made an attractive combination—man and horse.

'I do wish you hadn't destroyed my film,' she grumbled. 'I'm sure I had some good shots of you and Le Carpentier.'

'You can take some more if you like,' he surprised her by saying. 'Now that I know they won't be appearing alongside some vulgar article.'

'So you *do* believe me!' Claire was disproportionately pleased. 'I'm glad.'

'So am I.' Again he surprised her. 'I wouldn't like to think such loveliness concealed deceit.'

A warm glow invaded her being. Careful, she admonished herself: a man so experienced with women is also capable of flattering but insincere compliments.

She could easily have mounted Minou unaided, but before she could do so strong hands encircled her waist and lifted her bodily up into the saddle. Then Ross bent to adjust her stirrups, giving her a unique view of the top of his head and the way his thick hair sprang out from the crown.

Seen this way, from above, the exposed nape of his neck seemed to cry out for fingers to caress and shape it, and Claire was actually afraid for one moment that she would give in to the impulse. But even as she clenched her hands on the reins, he straightened up and swung himself lithely into his own saddle.

'Where are we going?' she asked as the horses moved off.

'We'll follow the valley, up-river.'

The valley in which the Moulin Gris stood, Ross told her as they clattered out of the yard, was only one of half a dozen small remote valleys in the area.

'The whole area is very sparsely populated. It varies between quiet secluded fertile regions and dramatic mountain peaks.' He pointed towards the distant mass of the Luberon. 'Be careful if you drive up into the mountains. The roads twist and turn and climb through quite spectacular landscape. But it can be extremely dangerous.'

'Don't you find it lonely?'

'No. I don't seek much social intercourse as a rule.' Immediately Claire felt that her presence must be an intrusion. But before she could comment, he went on, 'But I'm not a complete recluse. I do have a few tried and trusted friends, who respect my views.'

'Which are?'

'I should have thought I'd made that pretty plain,' he said drily. 'Chiefly that I'm entitled to my privacy. Visitors come to the Moulin Gris by invitation only. And that anyone who talks to the Press about me no longer counts as a friend.'

'Well, I assure you *I* shall respect your confidence,' Claire told him. Then, 'But you must be a very *successful* writer,' she couldn't resist adding.

He angled her a sharp glance. 'Why? Because the Press have tried to harass me?'

'That,' she agreed, 'but all this too—being able to afford to live abroad. Your horses, your hobbies— none of them cheap.'

'I'm moderately successful,' he said. 'But "all this", as you call it, wasn't paid for by my writing.' There was an odd note in his voice—one almost of distaste, which made her look at him.

'Oh,' she said doubtfully, 'I see.'

'No,' he disagreed pleasantly, 'you *don't* see—and I'm afraid you won't.'

He might not have intended it as such, but Claire felt snubbed. But then, on such brief acquaintance, she could hardly expect to be ranked among the intimate friends in whom, presumably, he had confided the details of his past.

'I'm sorry,' she said in aggrieved tones, 'but it's very difficult with you to know just which subjects are taboo.' She added ironically, 'Perhaps we'd better just confine ourselves to general topics—the weather, politics, et cetera.'

'God forbid we should descend to such triteness!' He had the grace to smile a wry apology. 'Forgive me, but I prefer to live in the present, taking each day as it comes, rather than dwelling on the past I've at last managed to put behind me. Maybe,' he added, 'you should do the same.' An oblique reference to her unhappy marriage.

'I intend to,' Claire said. 'But I also mean to learn from it.'

'Don't you think *I* have?' He was curt.

As Ross had said, their route followed the banks of the same river that flowed beneath the walls of the Moulin Gris.

'You wouldn't think it to look at it here, but it starts as a fast-flowing stream some four miles away,' he told her.

And as they rode Claire saw how it did indeed change in character. Almost placid at the millpond, upstream it gushed and spilled over waterfalls, continually changing colour as it swirled over black rocks, formed deep blue pools and crossed shallows where flourishing weeds turned the water a brilliant luminous green.

They dismounted, tethered their horses and sat on the hillside so that Claire could better drink in the sight.

'Beautiful but dangerous,' said Ross, but he did not seem to be looking at the river, and Claire felt a chill *frisson* skim down her spine. He couldn't mean her? No, why should he? But his description might almost have fitted Ross himself. Only she would have said *handsome* and dangerous.

He was taller and broader than Joe and his features were more refined. Joe had been ... well, rugged was the polite description. There were probably other differences too. But what did it matter? She was only here for three weeks. It was not as though she was likely to fall in love.

Besides, she had vowed that the next man, if there was one, would be quite quite different—shorter, stockier and blond. Yes, definitely blond, as unlike Joe as he possibly could be.

'You said you'd learned from the past,' Ross said after a while, his question uncannily echoing her thoughts. 'What in particular have you learned?'

Claire stared into the churning water. 'To be more wary of men, I suppose—until I really know them. I hadn't known Joe very long.' She shivered. 'There's no way I'd rush into marriage again. In fact, I'm not sure I'd *want* to marry again.'

She sensed that Ross was watching her closely. 'What about relationships?' he asked. 'You're too young and too attractive for total celibacy.'

Claire looked at him curiously. There was no mistaking the sincerity in his voice. But his implication troubled her a little. 'I don't go in for "relationships",' she told him.

'All or nothing, eh?' His tone was sceptical. 'A pretty drastic policy—if it's true.'

'It's true,' she retorted. 'Anyway,' sharply, 'it seems to suit *you*!'

'But then I'm older than you.'

'But not necessarily wiser,' she almost snapped. He purported not to be interested in her as a woman. Yet from time to time he seemed to make signals that nearly persuaded her to the contrary. Had he been deliberately misleading her? Was he hinting now that while he wasn't into permanent relationships he would not be averse to having an affair—with her?

Well, she wasn't going to be fooled. And neither would she succumb to such a suggestion. She was perfectly capable of handling any situation that might occur. She wasn't afraid of Ross Savage—at least, not in the way she had feared Joe.

No, an inner voice agreed. But you *are* afraid of yourself. You know you're peculiarly vulnerable to this Ross Savage—to his body chemistry. You recognised that right from the start.

OK. But that didn't mean she had to give in to the compulsion. She wasn't about to lay herself open to more suffering. Deliberately she changed the subject.

'It's lovely here, lovely but almost frightening, the river is so fierce. I wish I'd brought my camera with me—I usually take it everywhere. But perhaps I can come again, now I know the way. And speaking of cameras, can I really take some more photos of your house? And the horses? And——'

'Yes. But before you ask, *I* would prefer not to figure in your snapshots myself.'

'Oh!' Claire tried vainly to hide her disappointment. 'You still don't trust me, do you?' Without Ross her photographs would be less meaningful, like capturing the setting of a beautiful piece of jewellery without its central stone.

Ross smiled and moved towards her, and for an instant her heart fluttered, until she realised his intention was to help her remount Minou. 'I trust you,' he said, 'God knows why. I've been let down so many times. But there's something about you——' He broke off abruptly, then, 'It's just that I've been so much photographed in my life, and nowadays I have an absolute aversion to posing for even the most casual snapshots.'

What a mystery this man was, Claire thought as they turned their horses for home. Did he but know it, his deep reserve made him more interesting than if his life had been an open book to her.

The sun was at its zenith now, turning the sky from blue to burnt white. But though the heat and the glare were becoming uncomfortable, Claire was loath for the morning to be over. And it seemed Ross sensed her reluctance.

'How would it be,' he suggested, 'If we return via the caravan and collect your camera? The afternoon, when it's too hot to be outdoors, would be the ideal time to take your interior shots.'

'But surely you don't want me hanging about your house this afternoon,' Claire demurred. 'You must have work to do. I thought you'd just drop me off at the van and——'

'And just how did you propose to pass the hours until your cousin returns? The van will be hot and stuffy, and you certainly can't sit out. No, by far the best thing is for you to have lunch with me and take advantage of my air-conditioning.'

Claire was still doubtful. 'It's very kind of you. But I still feel it's an imposition. If I come, promise me you'll just go on as you would normally and forget I'm there.'

His smile was a wry one. '*That* might be rather difficult,' he said obscurely. But this time Claire refused to allow herself to try and fathom his underlying meaning.

It certainly was more pleasant, she thought, to while away the afternoon in the airy living quarters of the Moulin Gris. Its scrubbed wooden beams and off-white furnishings, broken only by buttercup-yellow cushions, reinforced the pleasant coolness of the mill's interior.

After lunch, served in the terracotta-tiled dining-room, she was left to her own devices with only a warning from Ross 'not to try that ankle too much.' She clicked away happily.

Off the living-room was Ross's study, where normally, she supposed, he would have been working at the black lacquer desk. Curiosity made her scan the titles on the booklined walls, but if she had been hoping for something that would tell her more about their enigmatic owner she was disappointed. In fact, the whole of the ground floor was remarkably free of trivia—not even a single family photograph.

But perhaps, she thought, as she hobbled up the open staircase to take an aerial shot of the ground floor, he kept such personal reminders in his bedroom.

There were many fascinating angles to be obtained from the open gallery, on to which several doors opened—presumably into bedrooms.

Claire wondered if she dared peep inside. In all honesty she knew Ross's sanction of her photography did not extend to the upper floor. But the temptation was irresistible. She would just look around the doors, she promised herself.

The first room she came to was obviously a spare room. But what a room, with its four-poster bed and delphinium-blue fabrics that echoed the colour of rough-painted walls.

She stood for a long while in rapt contemplation of this apartment, its pictures and ornaments. How she would love a room like that! Then, before moving on, she broke her own vow—albeit guiltily—not to take any photos. Just this one, she excused herself.

There was no mistaking Ross's room, with its masculine, almost sombre cream and brown décor—and that vast bed. She couldn't take her eyes off it.

But then she realised that her ankle was aching badly. She had been foolish to climb the stairs. She would sit on the edge of the bed—just for a moment, to rest. Firmly she banished an unwanted image of Ross in that bed.

As she rested she looked about her. Unlike the spare room, this was a spartan apartment, with no ornamentation, and again there were no photographs. Strange. Most people had family mementoes dotted around. Ross Savage certainly seemed to go to great lengths to conceal his past, she thought, uneasy for the first time at what it might be that he had to hide. Suppose he had some kind of criminal record?

So busy was she with this thought she did not hear his soft-footed approach.

'What the hell?'

Guiltily she spun round, and blanched as she saw the fury in his face. She cringed away, and her immediate response, learned from an older fear, was to lie. 'I... Oh, I'm sorry. I'm not prying, honestly. I...I needed the bathroom. And then my ankle——'

'That's what they all say. You're not the first female who's wheedled her way into my home, thinking the next step—to my bed—would be an easy one.' He took her arm in an iron grip and marched her out of his room. For once he showed no consideration for her awkward limping gait.

But Claire forgot pain in her fury at his accusation. 'You...you arrogant, conceited bastard! You *do* think you're God's gift to women, don't you? I don't know why—and I don't *want* to know why. But let me tell you, I wouldn't go half a mile to see you, let alone get in your bed. I told you, I was looking for the——'

'There's a cloakroom on the ground floor,' he told her grimly. 'As Madame Pierrepointe would have told you, had you bothered to ask.' And he marched her there.

She loitered longer than necessary in the cloakroom, fearful of facing his anger again. But when, finally, she did emerge, she found him coolly urbane once more. If there was anger it simmered beneath the surface.

'I'd like to leave now,' she said stiffly. 'I think I've outstayed my welcome.'

He did not argue. She would have been surprised if he had. He merely inclined his head. This time he did not attempt to carry her out to the car, but merely offered her his support. She could just about have managed without it, she thought as, tremulously, she set her hand on the muscular, hair-roughened forearm. But his expression dared her to refuse.

The hostile silence in the car was oppressive. It hung over Claire as unpleasantly as her guilt about that lie. It had been an instinctive response to fear, but—and Wanda's words came back to her—not every man was a Joe O'Reilly. And at least Ross had a right to his anger. She *had* been off limits. It would take all her courage, but she must confess. She owed him that much.

'Ross——' she began tentatively. But he chose that precise moment to speak, cutting across her nervous attempt.

'There's nothing I detest more than a liar,' he said tautly. 'But like a fool I allowed myself to be per-suaded that *you* were different. It seems even I still have lessons to learn about women.'

'Ross, please . . .' She choked on his name. 'Please let me explain——'

'Let you tell me more lies, you mean!' He was contemptuous. 'Save your breath!' He swung the car into the field. There was so little time left in which to convince him.

'OK!' As they neared the caravan Claire drew a deep breath in an attempt to steady her voice. She was perilously close to tears. 'OK, I *did* tell you a lie—I admit it. But——'

'Your admission comes a little late, but quite unnecessarily. I knew——'

'Listen to me!' Claire cried desperately. 'At least listen to me. I'm trying to apologise, if only you'll let me. To tell you why——'

'Oh, I fully intend to extract an explanation from you.' He was out of the car and round to the passenger side in one swift movement, almost as if he thought she would try to escape him. He must know she couldn't, Claire thought resentfully. The injury to her ankle had been confirmed by a doctor of his own choosing.

Her hands were trembling so much that she could not insert her key in the lock of the caravan door. With an impatient sound Ross snatched it from her, then swept her inside and closed the door behind him.

'Now!' he said grimly as Claire, her legs shaking too much to hold her, sank on to her bunk bed. 'Now we'll have the full story—about why you're here in Puit de Mirabeau, who sent you and...'

She was conscious of his voice going on and on as she stared blankly at him. Then light dawned. Oh no, he was back on *that* tack! Her foolish impulsive inquisitiveness at the millhouse had destroyed his every scrap of confidence in her. She tried to speak, failed, and to her consternation burst into tears.

'Stop it!' Ross grated. 'Stop it, do you hear me?' Through her distress she was aware of his voice crackling with anger. 'Don't think you can get away with it by turning on the waterworks. Too many women have tried that one on me.'

But Claire could not check her sobs. The cumulative stresses of the past year had lowered her resistance so much that once she had begun to cry it seemed impossible to stop.

'*Will—you—stop—that?*' His words were punctuated as his hands on her shoulders administered a series of violent shakes.

Fear zipped down Claire's spine. Joe had always reacted to tears with physical abuse. It was as though the sight of her weakness had spurred him on to greater excesses.

'Oh!' Tears could not hide the terror in her eyes as she cowered away, one arm lifted in a protective movement that all too clearly anticipated blows to come. 'Don't...don't hit me, please, Joe!' In her terror Ross and Joe had become one man, a composite of all male anger and retaliation.

The most extraordinary expression crossed Ross's face. His hands fell to his sides. He stared at her for a long second, his grey eyes full of a horror as great as her own. 'He actually used to *strike* you?' His voice was husky and a nerve throbbed agitatedly at his strong jawline.

'Yes.' It came out as a whisper. 'That's why...that's why I lied to you...about w-wanting the bathroom. You see, J-Joe n-never used to believe me, even when I was telling the truth. I...I knew I shouldn't be upstairs. B-but I wanted a view from the gallery. The d-doors were open...and I was t-tempted. And I'm sorry, be-because now it's ruined everything.'

Suddenly, heavily, Ross sat down beside her, his eyes still glazed, unseeing. 'And *that's* what you meant about lying to me?' he asked uncertainly.

'Yes.' Her voice was still low and her head hung down so that her hair hid her face. Crying made her ugly; she didn't want him to look at her.

But Ross had other ideas. The hand that grasped her small soft chin was gentle but firm, as he lifted her face and looked long and steadily into the tear-drenched green eyes.

'Claire, do you swear to me that *that* was your only lie?'

'Yes! Oh, yes!' Mesmerised by his gaze, his closeness, the touch of his hand, she stared back at him, willing him to believe, to trust her.

'And everything else you told me was true? You're *not* a photo-journalist?'

Thank God he hadn't asked about Wanda. 'I swear it,' Claire said. 'And oh, Ross, I'm sorry about . . . about the things I said to you back there.'

'Don't be,' he said surprisingly. 'It was only the truth anyway. But, Claire,' he put his hands on her shoulders again, gently this time, his fingers absently kneading away her tension, and his voice was suddenly husky again, 'there's no need for you to be afraid of *me*. I've been many things to many women in my time, but I've never, ever raised my hand to a woman. God, that husband of yours must have been an unmitigated swine!'

'He . . . it was a kind of illness, I suppose. I can see that now. But at the time . . .' under his sympathetic gaze her voice broke once more and her lips trembled '. . . at the time I was so . . . so afraid.'

Ross made a curious little sound in his throat and his hands slid from her shoulders and down her arms, his fingers painfully hard. But this time she was not afraid. His eyes seemed drawn to the quivering lips. Hers were focused with equal intensity on his well-shaped mouth. She had never expected to long like this again for a man's kiss.

There was a sudden tension in the atmosphere, but now it was not one of anger or of fear. The silence seemed charged with electricity. Warmth invaded Claire's body and her face. Her mouth was dry and the glitter of tears in her eyes was replaced by something else, something feverish and yearning.

It seemed to her that Ross's head was moving closer. With a little sigh, she closed her eyes and, her lips pouting an unconscious invitation, she swayed towards him.

'No!' The word exploded with violence from him. He pushed her away.

Her eyes flew open as he stood up and turned his back upon her.

'Ross?' she enquired tremulously.

'I'm sorry, Claire,' he said stiffly, 'but you seemed to be under the impression that I was about to kiss you.'

'Well, weren't you?' she challenged.

'*No!*' It seemed to be said with far more ferocity than the situation warranted. He moved towards the door.

'You're . . . you're not going?' Claire faltered.

'Yes.' He didn't even turn to look at her.

As the sound of the Citroën's engine faded into the distance, Claire still sat, arms wrapped tightly about herself in an effort to crush the sensations that still racked her. She didn't believe him. He *had* been about to kiss her, he *had*. And she had wanted him to—oh, so much!

It's just sexual, she tried to tell herself. I'm in no danger of falling in love with him. I mustn't do that.

It was just the way it had been when she'd first met Joe—before she had known what he was really like.

That powerful sensuality that had destroyed her reason. And look where that had got her. No. It mustn't happen again.

CHAPTER FOUR

IT WAS growing dusk when her cousin returned.

'I didn't expect to find *you* back yet,' Wanda said. 'Didn't you go out with Ross Savage?' Then, as Claire nodded, looking more closely at her, 'You've been crying. For Pete's sake, you're not still moping over that bloody Joe?' And without waiting for an answer, 'What you need is another man.' Then, with a note in her voice Claire did not understand, 'Though possibly not Ross Savage. And talking of men—have *I* had a great day!'

Wanda, it seemed, had cycled into Cadenet where, in the course of her sightseeing, she had met another tourist—male, of course—and had unhesitatingly paired up with him, going off with him in his car to Aix.

Even if it had not been for her unfortunate experience with Joe, Claire would never have dared to pick up a man the way Wanda did.

'And is *this* one married?' she asked curiously.

Wanda shrugged. 'God knows, I don't. Doesn't matter too much on holiday. He's a great laugh and free with his money, I've arranged to meet him again tomorrow. I presume you'll be riding again with your Mr Savage?'

Wanda sounded as if she hoped so, but Claire doubted it very much. Yet if she said no Wanda might feel she was asking her to cancel her own arrangements. Frankly, Claire couldn't see her doing it, not with a new man in her sights. But then neither did she want to tag along with Wanda—even if her ankle had been up to it. So she made a sound that could have meant either yes or no.

'And how *was* your day with your reclusive friend?' asked Wanda. 'Been taking more photos?' as Claire put a new film in her camera and carefully put the exposed one into its protective canister. 'Of Ross Savage, no doubt?'

'Actually, no,' Claire said. 'He doesn't like being photographed. But I did take some of the house.'

'Oh, you'll have to get one of him somehow,' Wanda said teasingly, 'for your holiday memoirs. No holiday is complete without a few male piccies.'

Claire wouldn't have put it quite like that, but Wanda was right in one sense. She, Claire, would dearly love a picture of Ross to take home with her. Foolish, no doubt, to have such an evocative reminder of someone so unobtainable, but she wanted it nevertheless.

'What does he look like?' Wanda wanted to know.

'Oh, good-looking, in a stern sort of way. In fact, at first he reminded me a bit of Joe. But he's not a bit like him in character. And then . . . Wanda, do you remember, at your house on Saturday, someone asked you about Graison Martell?'

'Yes? Why?' Wanda asked curtly.

'Well, I've only seen newspaper photos of Graison Martell, but Ross has a bit of a look of him too, except that Graison Martell was blond and blue-eyed. Ross is dark, going grey, and his eyes are grey.'

'Well, there you are, then,' Wanda scoffed, 'no resemblance at all. You'll have to creep up on Ross Savage with your telescopic lens,' she suggested. And then, 'There's a fast-developing service at a chemist in Cadenet. I'll drop your film in for you if you like.'

'Will they be open on a Sunday?'

'Apparently.'

Sunday. If she had been at home Claire would have been going to church. She wasn't especially religious, but her parents had always attended and somehow she had kept it up—in spite of Joe's jeers and his suspicious insistence that she must have other more urgent reasons for going. 'Fancy the vicar, do you—or is it one of his congregation?'

Yes, Sundays in England followed a certain routine. But what did you do in a remote village in France that didn't even boast its own church? Thank heaven she'd brought plenty of books with her.

In fact it was tempting, after Wanda had gone, to stay in bed, to sleep and read the day away. But that was the way of a slob.

'And you're not going to become a slob,' she told herself aloud. 'Just because you haven't got a man to dress up for.'

Consequently she dressed and made up with even more than her usual care. The pale green cotton dress with its full, flared skirt flattered her slim waist and made the most of her small firm breasts. Her hair shone even more aggressively copper from the vigorous brushing she gave it.

It was a change to be able to make the best of herself without exciting adverse comment. When they'd gone out together, Joe had complained if she didn't look good. He'd wanted her to dress up and look nice for him. But then he thought other men were taking too much notice of her. It was a no-win situation.

She looked at herself in the long mirror affixed to the wardrobe door.

'All dressed up and nowhere to go,' she jeered.

'Alas, poor Cinderella!' The voice made her jump.

Because the morning air was already warm and sultry she had opened the door of the van and Ross had come upon her unawares.

Startled, she said the first thing that came into her head. 'I didn't expect to see *you* again!'

'No.' Uninvited, he entered. 'No, I don't suppose you did.' And, on a rueful note, 'I didn't expect to be here myself.'

In spite of all her determination to remain unmoved by Ross, Claire couldn't take her eyes off him, and they were being drawn irresistibly to lean hips and strong taut thighs, outlined by the well-fitting tightness of his trousers. She caught her breath as she felt a familiar stirring in the pit of her stomach. Then guiltily she dragged her eyes away.

'Then why *are* you here?' she demanded bluntly.

He shrugged. 'Call it a social conscience. I was riding...' he gestured '...on the hills above, and I saw your cousin leave. It will be a long day for you alone. I presume she *will* be gone all day again?'

'Yes.' Involuntarily Claire sighed. 'But it doesn't matter,' she said hastily to compensate for the sigh. She didn't want him to think she was angling for his sympathy. 'We're both quite free to do as we please.'

'*She* is,' Ross said drily. 'But the opportunities are hardly equal, are they—with your ankle?'

'I'll be all right, really. And I'm not expecting to be invited to your house again,' she assured him.

'Prickly, aren't you?' he observed.

Claire gasped. That was rich, coming from him! 'Talk about the hedgehog calling the thistle black!' she retorted. 'You're probably the most prickly person I've ever met.'

To her astonishment, he laughed. '*Touché!* Look, Claire, maybe I over-reacted yesterday. I've come in pursuit of a truce. Reject it if you like, but, believe me, it's sincerely meant.' He offered his hand.

It would have been churlish to ignore it, or his gesture of friendship. She put her hand into his, but he did not immediately release it.

'Tell me you're not afraid of me, Claire,' he said urgently.' OK, I lose my temper from time to time. But I *can* control it.' Emphatically, he added, 'I'm *not* Joe, Claire.'

'I know,' she said softly.

'Friends again, then?' His fingers tightened around hers, their grip, firm and warm, sending a glow all through her body.

She released her hand and moved away from him so that he could not see the hectic colour in her cheeks. 'OK,' she said with a valiant attempt at casualness. 'Friends.'

'Good!' He came up behind her and rested his hands lightly on her shoulders. She wished he wouldn't do that; it made self-control so much harder. 'Madame Pierrepointe made a useful suggestion this morning. She said, "Perhaps the young ladies would like to go to the Sunday market." *Would* you like to go, Claire?'

She ought to have more pride than to leap at this first offer. 'Very much,' she heard herself saying.

'Excellent. I have Le Carpentier outside, but it won't take me long to get home and change. I'll pick you up in, say...' he consulted his wristwatch '...three-quarters of an hour?'

Despite the fact that she had just spent the best part of half an hour on her appearance, Claire fussed back and forth to the mirror half a dozen times before Ross returned. It was compulsive, and she scolded herself.

It doesn't matter a damn to him what you look like. You're a tourist who inconveniently had a mishap on his property. He's merely following his—what did he call it?—yes, 'social conscience'. He'd do the same if you were as plain as a pikestaff.

But plain Claire was not. Despite her homily to herself, excitement had animated her heart-shaped little face. And when she descended the caravan steps to Ross's car, her green eyes shone with a luminosity unusual of late. And though he made no comment—deliberately, she suspected, for fear of arousing misunderstanding—there was that in his usually enigmatic grey eyes which told her she was light years away from being unsightly.

'How far is it to this market?' she asked a little breathlessly, for, seated beside him, his arm brushing hers, she found herself with a sudden surprising lack of anything else to say.

'It's about ten kilometres up the valley—at Ferigoulet.'

He drove in silence for a while. And Claire, stealing surreptitious glances at his profile, wondered what he was thinking about to draw those frown lines between his eyes. When he did speak it made her jump, especially since he turned his head abruptly towards her and caught her speculative eyes upon him.

'What part of England do you come from, Claire?'

She relaxed. Obviously he had been seeking for some non-controversial subject to break the ice. 'I was born in Hampshire,' she volunteered, 'in a little town on the edge of the New Forest. But I live in London now—or I did,' she corrected herself. 'After my...my marriage broke up, I decided to sell the London flat.

The caravan is going to be my home in future. My work involves me in quite a lot of travelling, so it will be very convenient.'

'Are you divorced? Or just separated?'

'Divorced,' Claire said on a shuddering breath.

Ross angled her an abrupt glance. 'Why the sigh? Surely, if it was an unhappy marriage, you're better off out of it?'

'Oh, yes,' she agreed, 'and I know divorce doesn't carry such a stigma as it did in our grandparents' time, but . . .'

'But?' he said encouragingly.

'It's just that my mother and father had such a perfect marriage. So do my aunt and uncle. I'd always hoped mine would be the same. And despite the fact that everybody's assured me I wasn't to blame, I still have this feeling of . . . of failure.'

'Probably quite unnecessary,' Ross said. 'But as I don't know the facts . . .' His words, ending in the air on an upward note of enquiry, were obviously an invitation to confide, if she so wished.

There hadn't been many people to talk to about her unhappy relationship with Joe. Just the counsellor, her solicitor and Wanda—all of them women. It was tempting to seek an outsider's view—a man's opinion.

'There's not much to tell when you come right down to it. All our problems stemmed from my husband's jealousy. It . . . it made him violent.'

'It's a violent emotion, jealousy,' Ross agreed. And something in his tone made her look curiously at him.

'You sound as if you know all about it.'

'Oh, I do,' he said grimly. 'But go on. We're talking about you.'

'Well, the marriage guidance counsellor called it "emotional jealousy". She said it was probably because Joe had only had two really deep relationships in his life—with his mother and his wife.'

'He'd no male friends?' Ross asked.

'No. And that made him too dependent on *me*. I had to be everything to him and he expected to be everything to me.'

Ross gave a grunt of incredulity. 'I can't imagine such an attitude of mind. But it certainly sounds like a bad case of immaturity to me. And yet I'm surprised you resented it. I always thought that was every woman's ideal—to be the be-all and end-all of her husband's life.'

'Not mine,' Claire said positively.

'That makes you very unusual in my book.'

'Oh...' she shrugged '...some day maybe, in the very, very distant future, I'd like to love and be loved again. But I would never ever give up my personal freedom again.'

'And what exactly does that mean?' He sounded disapproving. 'Don't tell me you believe in the right to have affairs outside of marriage.'

'Certainly not!' Claire was indignant. 'I mean my right to come and go as I please. Joe used to ring me two or three times a day—just to make sure I was where I said I'd be. I couldn't exchange the most innocent remark with a man. He even hated me to have women friends. So gradually I lost touch with them all. He'd even resent the book I was reading, because it took my attention from him. Once, when I didn't hear him, he actually knocked the book from my hands.'

Once begun, the words came spilling out in a torrent. And at the end of it all she looked at Ross in shamefaced apology. 'I'm sorry. You shouldn't have started me off on that tack. What a complaining, bitchy woman you must think me!'

'Not at all.' He flashed her a brief smile. 'You've obviously had a tough time. Better to get all the poison out of your system than to brood on it. I've made *that* mistake myself in the past.'

'Oh?' she said interestedly, 'were *you* married once, then?'

His normally full lips were drawn into a tight thin line. 'No,' he said shortly. 'At least I escaped that disaster.' And then, with a note of relief in his voice— as though he was glad to avoid further discussion of the subject, 'We've arrived. This is Ferigoulet.'

Ferigoulet, a small town nestling in the shoulder of the hills, was full of the beguiling old houses, shut-tered and pantiled, that Claire was beginning to rec-ognise as typical of the country.

The name Ferigoulet, Ross told Claire, came from the old Provençal word for thyme, in which the area abounded. And indeed, as she stepped from the Citroën, the air was redolent with its perfume, which made Ferigoulet, like the rest of Provence in July, feel leisurely and somnolent. Yet the town hummed with activity.

The market was sited in and around the central square, the stalls crammed haphazardly along the street. All the scents of Provence were on sale, for as well as the thyme there was rosemary, basil, sage, oregano and marjoram. Jewellery was displayed side by side with fish, rough country bread, digital watches and a cardboard box full of mongrel puppies.

Alleyways overflowed with pots and pans, farm-wives with squawking chickens and flop-eared rabbits. Sellers of lottery tickets vied with gypsy girls selling lemons and long plaits of garlic, while stallholders held out free samples—slivers of warm pizza, pink ringlets of ham and sausages.

'A colourful sight, isn't it?' Ross remarked as Claire exclaimed delightedly and reached automatically for her camera. And for the next few moments she was happily engaged in recording the sights.

Ross, seeing her engrossed face, left her to her own devices and strolled away to look at a stall selling antiques. When Claire looked around in search of him and saw him in profile, absorbed in his inspection, she realised that this was the perfect opportunity.

'Catch him unawares, with your telescopic lens,' Wanda had said. Her hands trembling, in case he should move and spoil her chance or—even worse—should turn and catch her and veto the shot, Claire adjusted the settings of her camera.

With the lens at its fullest extent, Ross's head and shoulders filled the frame. It was perfect. Praying no one would choose that moment to step in front of her, she clicked the shutter, once and then again for luck. She drew in a deep breath of satisfaction. There, she had him! Whatever might happen—though after these three weeks she might never see him again—she had him, captured for all time.

She watched him for a little while longer, her forehead creased in thought. Hard to believe she had known Ross so short a time. Everything about him seemed so familiar. *Was* it just that fleeting resemblance to Joe? Or was it . . .?

She sighed, shrugged and moved on slowly, favouring her ankle, returning to other less important subjects so that when he rejoined her she might be found innocently employed.

'Enjoying yourself?' He caught her up just as she was accepting a sample of the baker's art. 'And hungry too, by the looks of it,' he added humorously.

'I'm ravenous,' she admitted. 'It's gone one o'clock and we had breakfast at an unearthly hour, because Wanda was so anxious to be off.'

'What does she do with herself all day?'

'She's found herself a boyfriend,' Claire said, unaware of the edge of disapproval to her voice.

Ross misread her tone. 'You sound as though you're jealous?'

'Heavens, no!' she said emphatically. 'I told you, I've sworn off men—for a very long time.'

'Hmm.' It was a doubtful sound, and Claire looked at him indignantly.

'You don't believe me, do you? Just because, yesterday, when I thought you...' She broke off, her cheeks flushing at the memory. 'Well, anyway, I was upset—you know I was. And people sometimes... sometimes...'

'Act instinctively,' he suggested helpfully.

'Yes. But that's all it was.'

'Of course,' he agreed with suspicious politeness. But Claire had no opportunity for further protestation. He went on immediately, 'Since you're hungry, suppose we eat?'

Ferigoulet boasted only two restaurants, both of them modest in size.

'That's why I left suggesting lunch until later,' Ross explained. 'One soon learns to avoid cafés at midday.' Then he added, with that flashing white smile, which Claire had witnessed so rarely, yet liked to see, 'The Provençal has a clock in his stomach. *On mange à midi*—and not a moment later.'

Even so, the one room was crowded. The other customers were all French, people from neighbouring villages, Ross told her, all in their Sunday best.

'I hope you're not one of these females constantly given to worrying about your figure. Because you're about to undergo a gastronomic experience.'

Claire shook her head ruefully. 'No, however much I eat I don't seem to put on weight. Joe was always telling me how "skinny" I was.'

'Suppose,' said Ross, with a note in his voice that she could not quite fathom, 'you stop remembering what *Joe* said and did. That's the past. You're young—what, twenty-two? Twenty-three? You have a whole future ahead of you. And *I* wouldn't describe you as skinny.'

'I'm twenty-six, actually. And you're right,' Claire sighed, 'I really must stop talking about Joe. It's just that occasionally something reminds me—usually something that rankles. But I promise to stop being so boring.' And, to show that she meant what she said, she added—with a sparkle of laughter in her eyes, 'How *would* you describe me?'

Oh, dear, obviously that had been the wrong thing to say too. Or maybe he thought she was being flirtatious, fishing for compliments.

'Slender would be more appropriate, don't you think?' he said curtly. 'And for God's sake, Claire, don't be coy. It doesn't suit you. I've always abhorred coyness in a woman.' And then, just as she was contemplating an indignant reply, 'Ah, the hors-d'oeuvre.'

These were served on a flat basketwork tray, and Claire could count at least fourteen different varieties, including tiny sardines fried in batter, marinated mushrooms and artichoke hearts. There were also slices of pâté and gherkins. The bread served with the pâté had a fine crisp crust. And there was wine.

'Châteauneuf du Pape,' said Ross, filling her glass. 'Unlike other parts of France, Provence can't boast any great names. But nevertheless there are many excellent wines, and this is one of my favourites. Good, isn't it?'

Claire had to agree. But almost from the very first sip she could feel the wine going to her head. She did not often drink and was therefore more vulnerable to its effects.

As the meal progressed she began to regard Ross through a rosy glow of euphoria. Maybe there was more to his kindness than 'social conscience'. Maybe he did like her—a little. She recalled the feel of his hand at her elbow as he'd guided her into the restaurant and steered her between the tables. Had it been mere polite attentiveness, or something more?

'What are you dreaming about?' he asked in amusement. 'Your eyes are positively glazed!' He leaned forward slightly. 'They're like great emeralds,' he said on a note of discovery.

Claire snapped back to earth. Heavens, what a good thing he was not a mind-reader—and perhaps not as observant as he might have been, or he would have recognised her expression for what it was—sheer happiness at being here—with him.

'I was just thinking that this is probably the best holiday I've ever had,' she said hastily. 'The last time I was abroad was in my teens, with my parents. I'd always hoped my work would take me to exotic locations, but so far it hasn't.'

'Yes, your work. I'd intended to ask what you do for a living. Evidently you weren't purely a housewife.'

'No, thank goodness,' Claire said with feeling. At the very idea of being cooped up in that flat which Joe had made a prison cell, she shuddered. She sometimes thought work had been the only thing that preserved her sanity. 'I'm a make-up artist,' she explained.

'*Oh?*' He was suddenly alert, intent. 'In what field? Films? TV?'

'TV.'

'Ah!' he exhaled. 'And you enjoy it?'

'Most of the time. The hours are long, and there's a lot of hanging about. And sometimes a lot of dashing about.' She could also have added that she was also expected to work anywhere, from sumptuous sitting-rooms to freezing fields.

'Do you encounter many celebrities?' He seemed deeply interested. Strange. She wouldn't have expected him—as an obvious celebrity himself and one who sought anonymity—to be much concerned with the famous.

'Now and again. Mostly my subjects are ordinary people—sometimes difficult, sometimes maddening, but mostly just anxious because they've never been on TV before.'

Their conversation was interrupted by the arrival of the main course—rosy slices of lamb, green beans and a golden potato and onion *galette*.

Despite Claire's protests, Ross refilled her glass with the dark and heady wine. 'Nonsense, a meal is nothing without the appropriate wine.'

For a while they ate in appreciative silence. But questions were forming endlessly in Claire's brain about this man. It was difficult, however, to know which subjects to avoid.

'You haven't told me anything yet about these hobbies of yours,' she said diffidently. 'You *did* say you don't mind talking about *them*?' Her anxiety not to offend must have been evident in her face and voice, for Ross smiled wryly. 'What an ogre you must think me!'

'Oh, no!' Claire said breathlessly, dazzled as always by that smile. 'You're entitled to guard your privacy— I quite understand. In my work I've learned to be discreet.' She grinned, a gamine-like grimace. 'Most show business people's faces are their fortune. It wouldn't do to reveal inside information about them—warts and all! Why should you be expected to tell a complete stranger all about yourself?'

'Hmm. It's a pity more people don't share your views. I could tell you...' He broke off. 'But I won't.' And then with a smile this time that held nothing back, 'Instead I'll tell you whatever you want to know— about my hobbies. Which shall it be?' Then, on an enquiring note as she did not answer, 'Claire?'

'Mmm? Yes? What?'

'Where were you *then*, for heaven's sake?'

'Oh,' she said bemusedly, 'I... I was thinking what a nice smile you have—when you smile properly. You should do it more often.'

'Hmm, thank you—I think. Though I rather suspect that's a backhanded compliment—letting me know that on the whole I'm a miserable, grim-faced so-and-so.'

'Oh, no!' Claire was aghast. And then she realised he was pulling her leg and she began to laugh.

'And *that*'s better too,' said Ross, leaning across the table to touch her cheek. 'It's the first time I've seen you laugh. And it's the first time,' he added wonderingly, 'that I've realised you had those two wholly delectable dimples.'

His forefinger against her cheek, the slight roughness of its skin on her smooth face, sent tremors of delight through her body. And when he did not immediately remove his hand but thoughtfully traced the outline of her jaw, Claire swallowed convulsively.

'Hey, what is this?' she said flippantly in an effort to conceal her reactions. 'A mutual admiration society?' And, glad of the diversion, 'Oh, look, here's our dessert. Oh, goodness!' Her tone became reverent as she saw that lemon sorbet, chocolate tart and *crème anglaise* shared a plate.

The arrival of the dessert dispelled the tension which in any case, Claire thought, she had probably imagined, and at her request Ross began to tell her about his current interest—in hot-air-ballooning.

'I took it up chiefly because I wanted to write about it. The hero in my next book is a compulsive adventurer—a Richard Branson type, if you like.'

'It sounds as though you are too,' Claire observed, as Ross described some of the tension and drama of the sport.

He grinned engagingly. 'I must admit I do thrive on adrenalin-charged situations.'

'Did you have lessons, or what?'

'Yes. And there are written tests too one has to pass before going solo, things like navigation and air-law, for example.'

'And now you have your own balloon?'

'Mmm. She's called *the Spirit of Provence*. Would you like me to show her to you some time?' He spoke with affectionate enthusiasm as though the craft were a woman.

'Oh, yes!' Her eyes sparkled, not merely at the prospect of seeing the balloon but because it promised her the certainty of seeing Ross again.

Perhaps she was being foolish, but, even though there would never be an intimate relationship between Ross Savage and herself, Claire felt that, as things were, there was no reason why she should not go on seeing him on a friendly basis. Yes, she would like that.

As to what would happen when her three weeks in Provence were over, she deliberately closed her mind.

The room was beginning to smell strongly now of coffee and Gitanes, the sunlight through the restaurant window turning the smoke into blue spirals above the diners' heads. Unconsciously, Claire, a non-smoker herself, must have grimaced with distaste, and Ross was quick to pick up the signal.

'Shall we go?' And as they left the restaurant, 'Do you want to look around the market any longer? Did you see anything that caught your fancy? You seem to be walking a little better today, but all the same, you'd better not overdo it.'

At Claire's request they did make another slow tour of the stalls, and she bought some material, bright colours in cheerful Provençal prints.

'I shall make myself some skirts,' she said, 'and when I wear them—in future summers—I'll always be reminded of this place.' And you, she added the silent rider.

'That sounds as if you're not likely to return?' It was said with apparent matter-of-factness, and try as she might, Claire could not read disappointment or indeed any other emotion into his words. But that shouldn't concern her, she told herself firmly.

'I don't suppose I'll be able to afford it,' she said with a cheerfulness she did not feel. 'I only managed it this year with Wanda's help.'

'*She's* not short of funds, then?' Ross probed. 'What line is she in?'

Claire had guessed this question must come eventually and she had given much preparatory thought to her answer, how she might steer a course between the—to him—unpalatable truth and the outright blatant lie she deplored.

'She's . . . er . . . she's involved in . . . in some kind of market research.' Well, it was true in a way. In her role as a freelance journalist, Wanda had to know her markets.

'Oh? I wouldn't have thought that paid too well,' Ross observed. Then, to her relief, he changed the subject, drawing her over to a stall selling jewellery of the semi-precious type. 'Here, if this is to be your one and only visit, you must have something more durable to remind you of Provence.'

Before she could protest that her budget would not run to such things, he had selected and paid for a pendant, fashioned in the shape of a sunflower, yellow stones forming the petals.

'Oh, but you shouldn't have! I can't possibly let you——'

'Of course you can!' He waved aside her embarrassed disclaimer. 'It's only an inexpensive trinket. Oblige me by accepting it.'

It was stiffly said, and Claire was afraid she might be guilty of bad manners if she protested further. 'Thank you very much,' she said formally. 'I shall . . . I shall treasure it.'

'Here, let me fasten it for you.' He took the slender chain and put it about her neck. His fingers, fumbling awkwardly with the tiny clasp, brushed against the soft nape of her neck, and her breath was expelled in a long shuddering sigh, her breasts rising and falling in tempo with the sound.

For a long moment his hands were still. And both Claire and the man behind her were immobile as though for a brief instant all time and movement had been suspended. Claire could feel her heart beating with suffocating rapidity.

It was Ross who broke jarringly across the moment, his voice harsh, his words abrupt. 'We've been here long enough. Time we started back—if you're quite ready.' It was an order, not a question.

'Yes, of course,' she muttered. 'You've . . . you've wasted quite enough of your day on me.' But the polite disclaimer anyone else might have offered was not forthcoming, and Claire's spirits, almost unnaturally high until now, plummeted accordingly. Ross Savage was a straightforward man, not given to cheap compliments. He said what he meant. It followed therefore that he agreed with her statement.

The ride back to Puit de Mirabeau was completed in almost total silence.

'Can I offer you afternoon tea?' Ross asked politely as they neared their goal.

'No, thank you.' Claire could be just as formal. 'I'd rather go straight back to the caravan, if you don't mind.'

'As you please.'

On previous occasions Ross had always been round to the passenger side to help her alight from the Citroën's deep bucket seats. This time he did not switch off the engine or move from behind the wheel, and Claire noted abstractedly that his hands were clenched so tightly on its rim that the knuckles showed white against the tanned flesh.

It was as though he was furiously angry about something, and she racked her brain to think what she might have said or done to annoy him. But she could think of nothing. Everything had been pleasantly normal until that moment when he had placed the pendant around her neck. She sighed. He must be a man of more sudden moods than she had realised.

'Thank you for a very nice day,' she said, feeling like a polite schoolgirl.

He inclined his dark head. 'A pleasure,' he rejoined, but his tone did not reflect any such emotion.

She opened the car door, hesitated, then as it seemed he had nothing more to say, she slid from the vehicle. 'G-Goodbye, then.'

Once more that inclination of the head, and then as she shut the door he accelerated rapidly away.

He'd mentioned nothing about seeing her again, Claire thought dismally as she unlocked the van door and climbed painfully inside. Her ankle was throbbing and she realised she *had* overdone things.

Well, it looked as though there would be plenty of days of rest left to her. Ross Savage had taken sudden inexplicable offence, and, if he was that moody a man, she reflected, she was better off without him. In Joe, she'd had enough of moody men to last her a lifetime.

Claire had been anticipating a long dreary evening with only her thoughts for company, but Wanda was back earlier than on the previous day, and for a moment Claire wondered if Wanda had fallen out with *her* boyfriend. But her cousin, when questioned, seemed cheerful enough.

'No, everything's fine. But I'm not seeing him for a couple of days. He has to go to Paris—on business. So I'm afraid you'll have to put up with having me around. I'll try not to cramp your style.'

'So your friend's not just a holidaymaker?'

'No.' But Wanda seemed disinclined to tell Claire just what her new friend did for a living. Untypically for a woman who liked to talk about herself and her own affairs, she seemed far more interested in Claire's day.

'Took a huff, did he?' she said thoughtfully at the end of Claire's account. 'You must have played your cards wrong somewhere. Did he make a pass, perhaps, and you gave him the brush-off?'

'Certainly not!' Claire said indignantly. 'There's nothing between me and Ross like that. Though,' she added thoughtfully, 'I must admit I'm surprised in a way that he *hasn't* tried anything. From his own account of himself he's been a bit of a womaniser in the past.'

'Oh?' Wanda was immediately all attention. 'Tell me more.' But when Claire repeated Ross's remark about being 'tired of kissing', Wanda seemed to find it disproportionately amusing. And, infuriatingly, she would not explain her amusement. 'By the way,' she changed the subject slightly, 'I had your photographs processed for you. Here!' And she tossed across a colourful folder.

Claire riffled through the contents. The shots had turned out well, and she looked forward to having her current film developed, since she now had her pictures of Ross Savage. 'Thanks, Wanda. How much do I owe...? Gosh, that's dear!' For she had caught sight of the attached invoice, which amounted to double what she had expected.

'No, you only owe me half that. I . . . I included a film of my own.'

Puzzled, Claire looked at her. 'I didn't think you'd brought a camera with you. You said you weren't interested in——'

'I'm not. I borrowed my friend's for a few shots. I . . . er . . . I wanted some of him.'

Claire nodded understandingly. The only photos she had ever seen her cousin display were snapshots of her various conquests. Of course Wanda would want to add this latest man to her collection. 'Can I have a look at yours?' she asked.

' 'Fraid not. I . . . I sent them home. I thought Mum might like to see them.'

Somehow, to Claire, Wanda's words did not ring true. Claire knew that her cousin was not given as a rule to confiding in her parents about her love-life, guessing rightly that they would not approve of her affairs with married men. But, mentally, Claire shrugged. It was really none of her business if Wanda wanted to be secretive about her own photos.

'I'm rather glad you'll be around for a couple of days,' she told her cousin. 'I don't suppose Ross will come looking for me again.' She sighed. 'Perhaps it's just as well. After all, there's no future in it.'

'Maybe not,' Wanda agreed. But then, with a strange expression on her face. 'But if he doesn't come looking for you, there's no reason why you shouldn't take the initiative, and go looking for him. In fact, I think you should.'

Claire frowned her puzzlement. The suggestion was against all her inclinations. 'Why should I, for heaven's sake?'

'Oh . . .' Wanda seemed to be searching for a good reason. Then, 'For the sake of your pride, girl. Never let the man do the brushing off. I always make it a matter of principle to be the one to administer the old heave-ho.'

CHAPTER FIVE

THERE was no way Claire could have brought herself to do as her cousin suggested. *Her* pride worked the other way about. *She* would never run after a man who so obviously did not want her—any more than she wanted him, she thought mutinously.

She seemed to be reminding herself more frequently of late of her resolve not to get involved in another relationship.

Besides, Ross had made his feelings quite clear on the subject of the women who *had* pursued him, and she did not want to be added to that unflattering catalogue. Just how many women had there been in his life? she couldn't help wondering.

Despite her resolution to put Ross Savage out of her mind and simply enjoy the rest of her holiday, Claire found the days that followed were strangely without zest. She had Wanda for company, of course. But sightseeing with her cousin was a very different matter from sightseeing with Ross.

Since Claire's ankle was still inclined to be weak, they drove everywhere, leaving early in the morning and returning very late at night. But for Claire the places they visited just did not possess the same magic.

She did not attempt to deceive herself as to the reason for this. The scenery was no whit less beautiful, the buildings no less interesting. The fault lay with her and was the cause of many self-scoldings.

You're behaving like a spoiled brat, she told herself on one occasion. Cutting off your nose to spite your face—determined not to enjoy yourself because you can't have what you want. Well, you can't have Ross dancing attendance on you, so that's that.

It did not help that Wanda seemed to be in a strange mood. She made constant references to Ross Savage and to her opinion that Claire should seek him out.

'After all, you've got a good excuse. He still has your bicycle. You could go and ask if it's been fixed yet.'

It was almost as though Wanda had some vested interest in her cousin's friendship with Ross, Claire thought, and the idea made her uneasy. *Did* Wanda have some devious plan of her own?

'No, Wanda,' she said firmly, 'but if you're worrying about what will happen when your friend gets back from Paris—don't. I shan't want to tag on—I'm quite capable of amusing myself. And I can manage without my bicycle. My ankle's improving more quickly than that doctor said it would, so I should be able to drive the van.'

'Suit yourself,' Wanda shrugged. She seemed annoyed. 'But I think you're a fool. All you'll have to show for your holiday is a few photos, and I don't suppose you've even managed to take any of him.'

'Well, that's where you're wrong,' Claire said triumphantly. 'I have. In fact, I was going to ask you to get them processed for me next time you're in Cadenet.'

At once Wanda's expression changed. 'Of course I will. And I'm sorry if I sounded a nag. But I am thinking of you—I want you to enjoy your holiday.'

'I *can* manage to enjoy myself without a man, you know,' Claire said, and then hastily, for fear she had sounded catty, 'That wasn't meant as a crack at you.'

*   *   *

But, despite her assertion of independence, Claire felt decidedly flat when she had seen her cousin off for her rendezvous.

Thoughtfully she flexed her ankle. *Was* it up to a few hours of driving? If she overworked it too soon and strained it further Wanda might have to drive all the way home at the end of their holiday, which would be rather unfair.

She was still deliberating when she heard a familiar sound. Surely her imagination wasn't playing her tricks? That *was* Ross's ancient Citroën pulling up outside?

Her first instinct was to rush to the door to confirm this delightful supposition, but then better sense prevailed. She sank back on to her bunk and snatched up the nearest book. If it was him she didn't want to appear eager. Play it cool, she told herself. But her heart was thumping madly in her chest, the hands holding the book were shaking, and it wasn't just the growing heat of the summer's morning that was making their palms decidedly sticky.

At the peremptory rap on the panel of the open door, she forced herself to speak absently, her unseeing eyes still on the book. 'Come in.'

She did not need to look up. Her senses immediately confirmed that it was Ross. His presence filled the confines of the van, carrying with it that familiar aura of male warmth and tangy cologne.

'So you *haven't* left.' His voice was harsh, and Claire did look up now, her expression registering surprise.

'No, of course not. Why should you think we had?' And then more anxiously as she scanned his taut features. 'Have you come to give us notice to quit or something?'

Hastily she examined her conscience for anything she might have said or done to warrant eviction.

'No.' It was said shortly and he remained staring down at her for what seemed a very long time. There was a strange tension in the atmosphere and her heart began to thump again. Her fingers tightened on the book she still held as though it were a shield.

'Ross, what's wrong?' she blurted. 'You look... You look...' But then she found there was no adequate description for the way he appeared to her.

It was almost as though he forced himself to relax, the tautness draining slowly out of his long frame as he lowered himself on to the bunk opposite.

He was casually dressed as always—in jeans today, and an open-necked shirt in bright blue, the colour of which, Claire registered inconsequentially, must surely be responsible for warming his normally cool grey eyes. For there *was* more warmth in them than usual as they regarded her.

The open neck of the shirt revealed that his bronzed torso was coated with a fine down, shades darker than his grey-flecked hair, and on this expanse Claire found her own gaze riveted as she wondered with a painful inner spasm how it would feel to lay her palms against that down in an intimate caress.

But it was a safer speculation—just—than allowing her eyes to drift downward again to the point where those well-cut but faded jeans hugged and moulded strong thighs.

'Nothing's wrong.' He spoke at last. 'I thought you'd left, because the van wasn't here the last two days.'

Claire swallowed spasmodically, regret welling up within her. He'd come in search of her and she hadn't

been here. Two whole days wasted when she might
have been enjoying his company!

'You haven't been driving, have you, with that
ankle?' If there was concern in his voice it was very
angry concern, Claire decided. As if he were speaking
to a foolhardy child.

'No, of course not. Wanda did the driving. But I
thought I might try today. I——'

'Where is your cousin?' Ross cut her short.

'Gone to meet her friend. He was away in Paris for
a couple of days, so——'

'So she had time to spare for *you*!' he interrupted
again, sarcastically this time. 'She sounds a selfish
woman, your cousin.' And then, before Claire could
utter a feeble disclaimer—because Wanda *could* be
selfish, 'Are you in a mood for *my* company today?'

It sounded almost as if he thought she'd been
avoiding him the past two days, when in fact she had
thought the reverse was the case. It almost sounded
too as though he'd minded. But that was so unlikely
an idea that she dismissed it at once.

'You really don't have to——' she began, but for
the third time she was not allowed to finish.

'I thought you were interested in seeing *the Spirit
of Provence*?'

Abruptly Claire's cool front slipped. 'Oh, I am.
I——'

'She's being prepared today for her next flight. But
if you can't spare the time...'

He knew damned well there was not that much to
occupy her.

'I think I might just fit it in!' It was her turn to be
sarcastic.

'Good. Come on, then.' He rose and made for the
door, turning on its threshold to deliver one of his

devastating smiles, a smile that this time held pure devilry, 'By the way,' he said, 'do you usually read books upside down?'

An appalled Claire looked down. It was true. For the whole duration of their conversation the book had been giving the lie to her deliberately casual manner. She hurled it from her.

On the steps of the van she paused. 'Do I need to dress any special way?'

'No. We won't be making an ascent today,' he told her.

Claire noted that 'we' with mixed feelings. Uppermost was gratification that he seemed automatically to have included her in his plans.

Underlying the pleasure was a *frisson* of apprehension. She had expressed envy when he had first spoken of his adventurous pursuits, but envy from a safe distance was one thing; the chance to emulate it was another.

'You'll need to wear something warmer when we do,' Ross went on. 'It's cooler up there.' He indicated the almost cloudless blue sky. 'But for now...' his eyes appraised her with embarrassing thoroughness '...you'll do fine. You're the only small woman I've met who looks good in shorts. Tall women are usually leggy enough to take them, but short women are often pear-shaped. You...' And something in his tone made her blush '...are perfectly proportioned.'

At first sight *the Spirit of Provence* was just a disappointingly limp stretch of purple nylon. It lay in a field behind the Moulin Gris, a field sheltered by a tall bank of trees. This, Ross told her, was the site from which it generally made its ascents.

'Shelter makes balloon inflation much easier—and trees are ideal for this, more so than buildings.'

The envelope, as Ross referred to it, had been spread out on the grass, and two men were checking it over with minute thoroughness for any damage.

'It would be pointless to discover a fault after take-off,' Ross explained.

As well as the balloon itself, there were the basket wires to be examined, fuel tanks and hoses to be passed free of leaks. Ross introduced Claire to the two men performing the checks, local friends of his who on flight days formed part of his ground crew.

'When *will* you be going up?' she asked.

'Tomorrow, I hope, if everything is satisfactory. Still fancy coming with me?' There was a note of challenge in his voice and a look in his eye that told her he half expected her to refuse.

Her small chin came up and, in a voice that was only slightly quavery, she said, 'Of course. Why not?'

Although she had done her best not to disturb her cousin, Claire dressed next morning to the accompaniment of Wanda's grumbling.

'Good God, Claire, it's only three-thirty!'

But as Ross had explained, balloon flights were best made in the early morning or the evening. 'To avoid thermals,' he explained, adding with that rare but impish grin, 'and I'm not referring to your choice of underwear!'

She was prepared too for the possibility that all this pre-dawn effort might be wasted. For Ross had told her it was not always possible to adhere rigidly to timetables.

'Weather conditions are the crucial factor. Light winds are essential. They're forecast for tomorrow, but weathermen are not infallible.'

There was no point in inviting Wanda to come and watch. Even if her cousin could have been persuaded out of her bed at this hour, she still showed a strange reluctance to encounter Ross Savage.

Despite her cousin's assurances to the contrary, Claire could not altogether discount her suspicion that Wanda and Ross had met in the past, and probably with an unsatisfactory outcome.

Was it possible, she wondered, that Wanda had been one of the rapacious women whom he deplored? She could imagine Wanda resenting a brush-off of the kind Ross could be capable of administering. So why stay in the neighbourhood and take the risk of an encounter?

The unanswered question made her uneasy, and she pushed it to the back of her mind.

As far as an inexperienced Claire could tell, weather conditions seemed perfect as she hurried along the road in the grey light of early morning. She had assured Ross that there was absolutely no need for him to collect her.

'I can walk that far now, and you'll be busy preparing.'

Despite her anticipation of the day ahead, she could not quite quell the jittery feeling in the pit of her stomach. She wasn't certain that she would not display fear when it came to the moment of take-off, and she wanted very much to impress Ross with her cool nerve. His approval was strangely important to her.

When she arrived at the field the ground crew were scurrying around and the balloon was already partly inflated, gradually growing and taking shape until it looked a bit like a giant marquee, wallowing and tugging against its restraints.

Ross came to greet her, with a nod of approval for her jeans—a providential purchase during one of her outings with Wanda—the woolly hat and the sweater which could be donned, as and when necessary, over her blouse.

'You'll need this too.' He handed her a crash helmet. 'Better make sure it fits.'

Claire laughed a little nervously. 'This makes it all seem rather dangerous,' she couldn't help saying.

'It's only dangerous without the proper precautions and equipment. But it's not too late to change your mind,' he added, 'if you're scared.'

But Claire had fought and won her battle with nerves. 'You don't get rid of me that easily,' she retorted.

It was time to raise the purple 'marquee' into an upright position, and she joined the crew to help in weighing it down as Ross fired a jet of hot air into the mouth of the envelope.

Then the critical moment came when she must join him in what looked suspiciously like a five-feet-by-four-feet laundry basket—each corner occupied by a cylinder of propane gas.

'It's n-not very big, is it?' she enquired somewhat tremulously as Ross held out a helping hand and drew her in beside him.

'Big enough,' he said, his fingers tightening on hers, a gesture that was meant to be reassuring but which somehow increased her agitation. 'And sturdy, so don't worry.'

Strangely enough it had not been the safety aspect that had prompted her comment. Rather it was the prospect of being confined with Ross in so small a space for goodness only knew how long. She was very aware of how attractive he looked this morning in the navy track-suit and top he had chosen to wear for their enterprise. The material looked invitingly soft to the touch, a softness that she knew only just concealed hard muscle beneath.

She sighed with exasperation. She must try to overcome her physical weakness towards this man. He would certainly not appreciate it if he ever came to know of it.

They were both in the basket now, Claire holding on tightly to its rim. The helpers on the outside were ordered to let go and almost immediately, it seemed, they were airborne. Claire could not repress a little squeal of alarm as the wind caught them and blew them sideways and the earth seemed to fall suddenly away.

Ross put a reassuring hand on her shoulder and squeezed it gently. 'You all right?' he asked.

Ashamed of that small revelation of fear, she turned to look up at him. 'Yes, I'm fine,' she said shakily. And then, amazingly, she was, as they soared into tranquillity over the Provençal countryside. A tranquillity punctuated only occasionally by a whoosh as Ross lit the burner.

'Where are we going?' belatedly she thought to ask, and was rewarded by an amused laugh.

'Wherever the wind takes us,' he said.

Her brief calm shattered, she stared up at him. 'You . . . you mean we can't control it?'

'Only to the extent of going up and down to avoid hazards. We don't have the control an aircraft pilot has over our direction of travel.'

'Th-then you've no idea where we'll end up— or . . . or when?'

'I can't tell you where. If the wind is blowing east, for example, there's no way we could go west. Don't look so worried, Claire, I'll take great care of you, I promise.'

And, as she relaxed again, warmed by the genuineness of his concern, he went on, 'And we've got radio contact with the ground crew. It's up to them to meet us wherever we happen to land.'

'I wasn't r-really worried,' she fibbed—she didn't want him to think her a feeble coward. 'But,' she admitted, 'I did wonder how we'd get back to Puit de Mirabeau.'

'No problem, and when is even easier,' Ross continued. 'If we needed to we *could* come down very quickly any time we like—by pulling the ripcord. Or we could go on as long as there's sufficient gas in the cylinders. Anyway,' he said bracingly, 'surely not knowing when or where you'll land adds to the sense of adventure?'

Then, as she felt compelled to nod agreement, he went on, in a slightly different tone, 'Apart from anything else, being up here is a marvellous escape from the tensions of the world.' And Claire, studying his profile, wondered just what tensions he sought to escape.

Despite any misgivings she might still have, Claire was impressed by the totally soundless progress of their transport. So silently were they travelling that country sounds from below reached them with amazing clarity—a dog's bark, the lowing of a cow.

'Time for a little ritual,' said Ross interrupting her musings. He held up a bottle of champagne. 'A pleasant custom observed by all balloonists, to celebrate a successful ascent.' He released the cork, firing it straight up into the skirt of the balloon.

'To us!' he toasted.

'To us!' she echoed, wishing that 'us' held a greater significance than it did.

Drinking a glass of champagne as they drifted over the countryside was easier than Claire would have thought, though she had a tendency to cling tightly to the basket.

But despite this precaution she was still totally fascinated by the passing panorama beneath. 'You certainly see things from a different perspective up here,' she remarked as they breezed over houses, trees, animals and even birds themselves. 'It's fantastic! I can't thank you enough.'

Ross smiled indulgently at her enthusiasm. 'I thought you'd like it. Did you bring your camera?'

'Oh, hell, no!' Claire rarely swore, and it was more a cry of anguish than an expletive. 'How on earth could I forget that? I *never* go anywhere without my camera. Oh, I could kick myself, missing an opportunity like this!'

'Relax!' he soothed. 'I'll take you up again.'

'Oh, Ross, will you really?' Anxious green eyes looked up into his. 'You promise?'

It was as if her earnestness discomfited him, for he moved away as far as the basket's dimensions would allow. 'Scout's honour,' he said lightly. Then, 'Look . . .' and he begun to point out for her benefit various local landmarks. 'Have you been to Aix yet?' he asked. 'Or to the coast?'

Claire shook her head. 'No. But Wanda's been and she said she's going there again today.'

'Pursuing her affair, no doubt?' It was lightly said, but she sensed the distaste beneath the words. Just what had occurred between Ross and all those women,

she wondered wistfully, to cause his complete re-
nunciation of her sex?

Somehow, now that she knew him a little better,
she found it difficult to believe in the picture he had
painted for her of a sated roué. Wasn't it more likely
that Ross—as she herself had done—had built up a
protective shell, following on some great hurt?

'I'll have to take you to Aix some time. I . . .' Then,
'Claire? What is it?' She hadn't realised that her
speculation had caused her eyes to fix on his with a
more than usual intensity, until he demanded, 'Why
are you looking at me like that?'

She flushed. 'Oh . . . oh, I'm sorry. I didn't mean
to . . . I was just thinking . . .'

'Judging by your expression, your thoughts must
have been worth more than the proverbial penny. Care
to share them?'

She sighed. 'No. You wouldn't like them.'

'Try me,' he invited, and, though she still regarded
him doubtfully, something in his manner persuaded
her to venture.

'All right. I can't help wondering what happened
to you to make you want to withdraw from the
world—and from women. You told me once I was too
young to remain celibate. But what about you?
Surely——?'

'Oh, yes!' It was said somewhat grimly. 'I have all
the normal urges, my dear Claire, perhaps more than
my fair share of them.'

A quiver ran through her at his words, but even
more so at something in his expression. She could believe him. She had always sensed somehow that his
sexuality was not far from the surface, barely kept in
check by whatever inhibitions rode him.

She had a reckless urge to go on tiptoe and lift her mouth to his, to kiss away his hurt, and her hands clenched at her side as she quelled the impulse.

'Then why...? Did...did someone let you down badly?'

'You could say that. But that wasn't the only reason for my decision to give up...' He broke off as if he had nearly said more than he intended.

'Don't you ever get lonely?' Claire asked curiously.

When she had first separated from Joe it had been bliss to be alone, to be mistress once more of her own life—and more especially her own body. But of late she had begun to realise she was not a solitary by nature. Her whole being craved for someone with whom she could share not only intellectually but physically.

Of late? Face the truth, she told herself. It's only since you met Ross Savage.

'Lonely?' Ross queried. 'I have plenty of friends here in Provence, if that's what you mean? But,' softly, 'that *wasn't* what you meant, was it, Claire?'

He was looking at her intently, as he had so often done before, but this time there was something very different about the grey eyes. As they held hers, Claire became totally oblivious to her whereabouts. Suspended between heaven and earth, she felt suddenly closer to heaven.

Ross was still speaking, his voice husky, almost intimate. 'What you meant, Claire, was do I sometimes long for a woman in my bed. Wasn't it?' he challenged.

She swallowed. There had never been too much space between them in the basket. And now that space seemed even more reduced. But she faced him courageously. 'Yes, all right, that *is* what I mean.

But...but,' with a sudden feeling of panic, 'you don't have to answer if you'd rather not.'

'Oh, I'll answer your question, Claire.'

She was leaning against the side of the basket, and as a sudden disturbance made their craft jolt, he steadied himself by placing his hands on her shoulders—and then did not take them away. To him the gesture probably meant nothing, and Claire felt she would die of shame if he guessed the effect his proximity was having on her.

'I'll answer your question,' he repeated slowly, his gaze boring into hers. 'There are times, Claire, when I can't sleep, when my needs keep me awake, when the only thing I can do is to get up and go out, walk or ride until fatigue dulls those urges.'

His hands slid inwards along her shoulders and gently encircled her neck, his thumbs subtly caressing the soft sensitive skin behind her ears.

'And there are times like this...' it was almost a groan '...when I have to fight even harder to combat those desires.'

Claire had to make two or three attempts to find her voice before she could speak. 'M-Must it always be like that?' she said, unaware that her tone was pleading with him. 'Won't you ever allow yourself to...to...?' She couldn't say it, and to cover her embarrassment she began to trace the motif on his tracksuit top. It was a mistake. Even with the lightest touch of her finger she could feel the hardness of his ribs through the soft material, his regular heartbeat.

'To make love to a woman?' He completed her sentence for her, but it was not quite what she had meant.

She had been going to say 'fall in love'. Falling in love and making love could be two very different, separate things. Mutely she shook her head, not in negation of his words but at herself and her own confused emotions.

'Don't you see, Claire?' he went on throatily. 'Once I give in to that need, I may become ensnared again. To indulge the fire of appetite doesn't dull it. It merely feeds the flames until they want to consume more—and more.'

She stared at him, seeing the strength of the feelings that he was bottling up, and a spasm convulsed her stomach.

His hands were cupping her face now and his gaze was on her lips, as they parted in unconscious invitation.

'If I were to kiss you now, Claire,' he told her, 'I couldn't guarantee it would stop there. I... Damn!' he swore, and released her abruptly as his two-way radio crackled a summons. 'Yes?' he grated, and then, 'I see. Very well. Thanks.' And to Claire, 'Henri says there's a strong wind getting up. Time to go down.'

Claire, the rising bubble of excitement so rudely deflated, looked automatically for her watch and found she had forgotten to wear it.

Ross showed her his own wristwatch. Could it possibly be so long since take-off? The time seemed to have evaporated far too fast. 'We have to conserve some gas to control our descent.' His mood had veered completely. Once more he was tautly in charge of himself.

She fought back the ache of longing he had aroused in her and tried to match his tone. 'What happens exactly?' she asked.

'We allow the air in the canopy to cool, so we lose altitude. And remember, Claire, when we hit the ground, on no account must we allow ourselves to be

tipped out of the basket, otherwise the balloon will
shoot up again and we'll lose her.'

'*Hit* the ground?' Claire picked on the—to her—
operative word.

'It's not always a gentle process,' Ross admitted,
'especially if there *is* a strong wind getting up. But
don't worry, the basket takes all the shock.'

And suddenly they were sinking fast. To Claire it
seemed the earth was rushing up to meet them. When
they were only a few feet off the ground, Ross gave
frequent little bursts on the burner, in an attempt to
stabilise the balloon as it reached the landing field.

But Henri had been right about the wind. Claire
could not estimate its force for herself, but Ross, with
more experience, put it at about thirty miles an hour.
They were being carried fast across the field he had
chosen, and to her horror Claire saw that an enormous
tree stood in their path. A little scream escaped her,
and with no time to consider the consequences, she
flung herself at Ross, clinging to him.

Much later he confessed that it was only pure chance
that their basket missed the potentially disastrous
collision. Even as it was, a branch struck his head a
glancing blow, and as they finally jarred to a halt
Claire realised the man beneath her was unconscious,
blood trickling from a wound at his temple.

Her immediate instinct was to blame herself. If she
had not thrown herself at him like that, he might have
been able to avoid the injury to his head.

For a moment she felt sick and faint. But this was
no time to indulge herself in histrionics. She bit hard
on her lip and fought back the feeling of nausea.

Although she was concerned for Ross, at least she was almost sure he was only stunned. And she had an important task before she could give him her full attention. If the balloon were to be caught up by the wind again he might be dragged and injured further.

Praying that his weight alone was sufficient to hold the basket down, she slid over the side and crawled the length of the envelope, pressing it with hands and knees until all the air had been squeezed out of it. Thank God Ross had described this process to her, and thank God too that Ross himself had switched off the burner.

At last she could return to him. Back in the basket she leaned over him and put her hand against his cheek, tapping it lightly.

'Ross! Ross?' And then, when he still did not respond, 'Oh, Ross, please!' Suppose he was hurt worse than she had thought? A little sob escaped her, and she closed her eyes against the threatening tears.

'It's all right!' His deep voice was a little unsteady, then, strengthening, 'It's all right, you goose, I'm still alive.'

'Oh, Ross!' Laughter mingled with tears. 'I thought . . . I thought . . .' And then she felt his comforting warmth as he pulled her close. Her head against his shoulder, she tried vainly to control herself.

To her astonishment she felt his lips brush the top of her head. 'It's OK, Claire. Don't cry, my dear. Everything's all right now. I'm sorry your first flight had such a rough ending.' Then, wonderingly, 'Your hair . . . it's so silky . . . so sweet-smelling.' He buried his face in it, and Claire wasn't quite sure which of them was trembling.

She lifted her face to look at him and at once his mouth came down on hers in a long quiet kiss. With a little sigh of delight she surrendered herself to the warmth that enveloped her. Her lips clung to his and she wanted the kiss to go on and on.

How good it was to be close to him at last like this! No other thoughts intruded. She only knew that this was where she wanted to be and that she felt happier and more secure than she had for a long, long time.

But the kiss was growing more urgent. 'Claire!' Ross's voice came thickly. 'Let's get out of this...this contraption. There's no room to move.' He rose then, lifting her over the side of the basket.

He set her down on her feet and held her hard against him, the soft material of his track-suit failing to disguise his arousal. 'I knew,' he told her fiercely, 'that if I once kissed you it wouldn't be enough. I knew that the first moment I saw you. And I've been fighting it ever since.' Against her mouth he muttered, 'God knows I didn't want this to happen. But now it has...' His hands tightened on her hips and she caught her breath at the thrust of his, hard and demanding. 'I want you, Claire.'

Joe had used to say that—but with him it had been emotional blackmail. The very thing she had sworn never to fall for again. And yet, 'Oh, Ross,' she said weakly, 'I——'

What she might have said, how far she might have committed herself, she was not to know. For the moment was destroyed by the long-drawn-out braying of a horn as a Land Rover and trailer bumped across the field towards them, the retrieve crew shouting and waving. And with a jolt almost as fierce as that with which they had landed, Claire was brought down to earth once more.

CHAPTER SIX

Ross was greatly displeased, Claire recognised, at being caught kissing his passenger. He responded to the winks and wolf-whistles of the six Frenchmen with a taut smile and was at once all prosaic efficiency, overseeing the dismantling of the balloon and its bestowal in the trailer.

His friends' enquiries about his near-disastrous landing and the injury to his head he brushed impatiently aside as being 'nothing to worry about'.

Claire, reduced to the role of mere onlooker, felt black depression engulfing her. For a while there she had begun to think Ross was actually thawing towards her, that she might have succeeded where other women had failed.

But now she realised that there was another, more likely reason for his untypical behaviour. She had heard that narrow escapes from danger sometimes acted as a powerful aphrodisiac on the participants. And this must be what had happened to her and Ross.

To Ross, yes. But she knew with shameful certainty that for her there had been no need for such an external stimulant. It had crept up on her insidiously, despite all her efforts to resist it. Love. She was fathoms deep in love with Ross Savage. And she hadn't a hope in hell of his falling in love with her.

'Claire come on! We're ready.' Ross's voice, curt and brittle, cut across her despair.

Five men piled into the trailer with the balloon. But Claire found that she was expected to sit wedged between the sixth man and Ross who, despite the concerned protests of his friends, had insisted on driving the Land Rover.

How strange, to be equally close to two men, shoulder to shoulder, thigh to thigh. And yet one of those men might not have existed, for all his effect upon her.

Whereas Ross . . . Oh, God. What exquisite torture, to be aware of the masculine warmth and scent of him, to feel his breath fan her cheek as he spoke across her to the other man. But he did not address one word to her throughout the whole of their long journey back to Puit de Mirabeau.

She stared straight ahead through the windscreen, their conversation scarcely penetrating her consciousness as she relived those all too brief moments in Ross's arms.

What would happen when they did reach Puit de Mirabeau? It would be late afternoon, even early evening, by then. Would he just bid her a courteous farewell at the caravan steps? It seemed unlikely, she thought miserably, that he would invite her into his house and take up where they had been interrupted.

She was confirmed in her pessimism. For, instead of taking the shorter route back to the Moulin Gris, the Land Rover made the longer detour, in order to pass the camping site. But as the vehicle slowed by the open gate, Claire drew in a surprised breath. For the motor-caravan was no longer there.

Ross muttered something which, though inaudible, was obviously not an expression of pleasure, and the gearbox grated harshly before the Land Rover gathered speed once more.

'I'm sorry,' Claire apologised tremulously. 'Wanda usually rides her bicycle into Cadenet to meet her friend. She must have decided to use the van today. I don't mind waiting until she——'

'Standing about in a field, possibly for hours,' Ross said curtly. 'I think not.'

She had never felt so mortified in her life. Ross was all too obviously anxious to be rid of her, but equally obviously he felt obliged to offer her shelter until her cousin saw fit to return. Claire felt both unhappy and angry—but with whom she was angry she was not quite sure.

Nominally, until the London flat was sold and she could repay her cousin, the motor-home belonged to Wanda, and Wanda was perfectly within her rights to use it whenever she liked. She must have expected to be back long before Claire returned.

At the millhouse, Ross relinquished the Land Rover to the ground crew and ushered her indoors.

'I'll get Madame Pierrepointe to rustle us up a meal. Would you like to shower first?'

'If. . . if it's no trouble?' Her morale at low ebb, Claire wondered if she looked as grubby and dishevelled as she felt.

'Trouble? Why should it be?' But his tone was not very friendly, she thought sadly.

'Use the blue room,' he directed her, 'at the top of the stairs. You'll find it has its own en-suite bathroom.'

The direction had not been necessary. From her il-licit explorations, she knew all too well where the blue room lay, but she had never thought to set foot in it again.

On the previous occasion she had not noticed the communicating door, blending as it did with the sur-rounding décor. The bathroom, she found, echoed the delphinium-blue of the bedroom, its modern plumbing contrasting sharply with the antiquity of the outer room and the fourposter bed.

Leaving her clothes on the bedroom chair, she walked naked into the bathroom, the carpets luxuriously thick and soft beneath her feet. Being a realist, she had never longed for or expected wealth. But she felt she could happily live in this kind of style.

As the powerful jets of the shower beat a regular tattoo on her slender body, she felt some of the tensions caused by the day and by Ross's inconsistent behaviour draining away.

Now she was able to tell herself that it was just as well she and Ross had been interrupted by his friends' arrival. Another moment or two and she knew she would have said too much, revealing the state of her feelings. At least she had been spared that humiliation, since Ross had seen fit to withdraw into his former shell of reserve.

As soon as they had eaten dinner she would walk down to the field again, to see if Wanda had returned. And if she hadn't? Well, it wouldn't be too bad waiting for a while at this time of year. And Wanda was sure to be back before dark. Claire knew her cousin did not like driving at night.

She stepped from the shower, dried herself on one of the enormous fluffy blue towels and anointed her body with the sweet-smelling oils thoughtfully provided. Then, with the towel wrapped about her, she went back into the bedroom—and stopped short in surprise. Her clothes had disappeared. Instead, on the chair where she had left them, there lay a silky robe.

A woman's robe, she discovered as she picked it up, but a woman who must be several inches taller than herself. And she was swamped by a fierce sensation that she recognised as jealousy. To whom did the robe belong?

She found herself extremely reluctant to put the garment on. It was not merely that it had been worn by someone else. In years gone by—before her marriage—to stretch their budgets she and her friends had freely borrowed and exchanged clothes. No, her reluctance stemmed from the fact that the robe had been used by a previous woman in Ross's life.

What arrogance! Immediately she scoffed at herself. Seeing that you're not even the *current* woman in his life. You're nothing, she taunted herself, just a passing acquaintance.

He said he *wanted* you, arrogance replied.

Rubbish. At that moment, in the exhilaration of escape from disaster, *any* woman would have served his purpose.

Abandoning this fruitless argument with herself, she discarded the bathtowel and put on the offending robe, hitching it up and belting it tightly around her slim waist, sternly ignoring her body's outraged quiver of distaste.

But now what? Was she supposed to leave the bedroom and go downstairs dressed like this?

Well, she certainly wasn't going to stay here until Ross had to come looking for her. That course of action might well be misconstrued. Taking a deep, steadying breath, she opened the bedroom door, stepped out on to the landing and, clutching the robe, began cautiously to descend the stairs.

'Ah, there you are! I was beginning to wonder if you'd drowned.' At the foot of the stairs Ross, in his everyday clothes of jeans and open-necked shirt, his hair still wet from the shower, looked up at her.

At the sight of him her footsteps faltered and stopped. Every time she saw him there was this fresh assault on her senses. She rushed into garbled speech. 'I . . . my clothes . . . I couldn't find——'

'Don't panic—nothing to do with me. *Madame* has removed them—her fastidious soul noted the dirt and grass stains. They'll be returned to you tomorrow, immaculate as new.'

'It's very good of her, but what am I supposed to wear until then?' Claire enquired.

'No problem. After we've eaten, I'll take a walk down to the field and see if your cousin has returned—and ask her to give me a change of clothes for you.'

'Oh, no!' she said hastily, continuing her descent of the stairs. 'You mustn't do that!'

'And why not?'

She couldn't think of any good reason, other than her private conviction, based on her cousin's strange behaviour, that Wanda and Ross must not meet. And she couldn't tell him that.

She was saved from mental invention. The robe, far too long for her, escaped the confines of its belt and effectively tripped her, catapulting her the last few steps into Ross's arms.

He staggered slightly under the unexpected impact, then steadied himself and her. As he did so, Claire felt the inexplicable brush of warm flesh against her midriff, and looking down she discovered with a little thrill of horror that the edges of the robe had fallen apart, revealing that she wore absolutely nothing beneath it. Worse still, the nipples of her exposed breasts were taut and erect, mirroring his effect upon her.

Ross had discovered that too. As she struggled to release herself from his clasp, a strangled sound escaped from his throat, 'Claire, I——'

'*Monsieur, mademoiselle*, the soup is——' Madame Pierrepointe, bustling in, a tray in her hands, halted and coloured to the roots of her iron-grey hair at the sight of her employer and his guest in what must seem a very intimate situation. She turned aside and hurried into the dining area.

Freed abruptly from Ross's clasp, Claire snatched at the robe and refastened it with shaking hands. She felt a cowardly impulse to run back upstairs and hide herself, both from Ross's arrested grey gaze and Madame Pierrepointe's embarrassment.

She might have fled, but Ross, recovering more quickly than she, put a firm hand beneath her elbow and steered her towards the table where two large bowls of fragrant-smelling soup awaited them.

'There will be chicken and salad to follow, *monsieur*,' *madame* announced. The colour had still not faded from the housekeeper's face and Claire was glad when she bustled away.

She had to say something to break the tension. 'Wh-whatever must your housekeeper think?' she blurted.

Unexpectedly Ross gave a wry smile. 'Undoubtedly she'll be thinking that I've at last begun to behave normally. I imagine that *madame*, being a Frenchwoman, finds it hard to conceive of a man who lives alone, without *"l'amour"*.'

'You mean,' Claire squeaked, 'she thinks...she thinks...'

'That I've taken a mistress? Yes.'

A mistress. Claire's heart sank to an all-time low. Of course Ross would think of it in that light. He wasn't likely to be visualising her in terms of anything more permanent. The tasty soup might have been ashes in her mouth.

'Don't look so shattered,' he told her. 'She'll soon find out she's wrong.'

Claire stared down at her food. Worse and worse. Now he was adding injury to insult—or the other way about. She was appalled to find herself thinking that it would be more flattering to be desired as a mistress than as nothing at all.

But Ross seemed blithely unaware that he had just driven the final nail into the coffin of her hopes. 'I hope our little hiccup today hasn't given you a distaste for ballooning?'

'No,' she said in a low voice. Not that it mattered. She wouldn't be going up with him again. Oh, he'd promised her another flight, but it would be more sensible of her to refuse. It would be even more sensible not to see him again. He had too much power to hurt her, a weapon she had sworn not to put in any man's hands again.

'What's the matter, Claire?' His voice was gentle, and with a start she found that he had come round the table to stand beside her, his hand on her shoulder. 'You *did* enjoy today, didn't you?'

'Of course,' she said, not quite able to trust herself to say more. She had enjoyed it—far too much. That was the trouble. Not just the flight itself, but the magic of being alone with him—totally alone, far removed from the everyday world. And she had discovered she wanted it to be like that always, for the rest of her life.

'Claire, are you angry with me for some reason?' Ross probed. His hand was still on her shoulder, kneading it slightly. He could not help but be aware of the tension in her.

Dumbly, she shook her head, and with a little exclamation of irritation he used his free hand to take hold of her chin and force her face up, so that he could see it.

Quickly Claire closed her eyes, but not before he had seen the glitter of tears in them.

'What *is* it?' he puzzled, and bent over her just as Madame Pierrepointe returned with the salad.

'Damn and blast!' he swore vigorously, and strode back to his own seat.

'*Je regrette, monsieur, mais je——*' Madame Pierrepointe stammered apologetically. Obviously she believed she had once again interrupted a tender scene.

'It's all right, *madame.*' At once Ross had a contrite smile for her. 'I was not swearing at you, but at myself.'

The salad was good, the chicken succulent and tender. But Claire had to force herself to eat. Oh, let Wanda come back soon, she prayed. Let me get away. And yet there would be no privacy in the caravan to give rein to her emotions.

At least Ross made no further attempts at interrogation, and Madame Pierrepointe was able to bring in the dessert without further loss of countenance.

The uneasy silence continued through the serving and drinking of coffee, and Claire felt her nerves stretching to screaming point. If only she had her clothes she could have got up and walked away from this situation and from the Moulin Gris. As it was, she was dependent upon Ross's good will and offices for her departure.

'I . . . I should think Wanda will be back by now,' she said when at last she could stand the brooding silence no longer. She glanced towards the un-curtained windows, which showed a sky almost to-tally devoid of light. 'She . . . she doesn't like driving in the dark.'

'In that case,' Ross said, 'I'll walk down and——'

'C-Couldn't you just drive me there?' she asked. 'Surely that would be less——?'

'No.' He spoke abruptly. 'I think it would be better if you were dressed when . . . when . . .' He did not complete his sentence, but stood up, pushing his chair back so hard that it almost tipped over. Then he went on, as though he could not help himself. 'The thought of you,' he grated, 'beside me, naked under that robe, might be altogether too much for my self-control.'

Claire stared at his retreating back view. His words had rearoused all her own painfully doused longings. It was probably just as well, she reflected, that Ross was capable of such iron self-denial. She had a feeling that if he had again attempted to make love to her, *she* would have no such adequate defence against *him*.

In his absence she wandered into the comfortable living area and curled up in the corner of a couch. The atmosphere of the room soothed her ravaged feelings. What an utterly delightful place this was!

For just this short while she would indulge herself in a fantasy. That she belonged here; that she was married to Ross and only awaited his return to be carried upstairs to that sombre bedchamber of his—or perhaps to the more evocative environment of the blue room—where he would make long and ardent love to her—where she would reach heights of ecstasy and fulfilment she had never known but could only imagine.

For it would be so different from her marriage to Joe. He had been a sensual man and she could not

deny that, in the early days of her marriage, she had
enjoyed sex. But that was all it had been—a physical
thing, its appeal soon destroyed by Joe's jealousy, his
violent behaviour. She knew now that there had been
no spiritual depth to their relationship, no true
emotional commitment. It had not been love.

But she was not allowed to dream for long. Madame
Pierrepointe, back and forth clearing the table, seemed
disposed to chat.

'I apologise for my unfortunate intrusions,
mademoiselle. But me, I am so 'appy for you and
monsieur. For too long he has been a lonely man.'

'Oh, but...I...we...*madame*, please, you mustn't
think...' Claire was anxious to dispel *madame's* mis-
taken notions. She was not given the chance.

'Me, I am 'appy of course to continue to work for
monsieur. But, you understand, I come in only by
day. Me and Gaston, we 'ave our own little 'ouse in
the village. Le Moulin Gris needs a mistress. It needs
children to make it an 'ome.'

Claire hoped Ross had not overhead this final
speech as he strode back into the room, looking remarkably like he had at their first encounter, black-
browed and angry.

'That damned cousin of yours isn't back yet!
Selfish, inconsiderate——'

'Oh, dear!' Claire exclaimed anxiously. 'I do hope
there hasn't been an accident.'

His features relaxed. 'Now isn't that just like you—
to be more concerned for her than for yourself? Well,
it settles one thing. You'll have to stay the night.' He
sounded as though the prospect did not enchant him.

'*Oh!*' Dismay warred with an insidious feeling of
excitement. Despite all her sensible strictures to
herself, she was still reluctant to end their association.

He misunderstood her reactions. 'You needn't worry,' he said harshly. 'Despite all evidence to the contrary, I can control myself. And I have no intention of forcing myself on you while you're under my roof. All the bedroom doors have locks, if you feel it necessary to protect yourself.'

Well! He need not make it so bitterly obvious that his distaste for her sex had not been vanquished. In fact, Claire thought resentfully, he was probably blaming her for his recent lapse into sensuality. Well, he should have no cause to blame her any further.

'In that case,' she said, rising to her feet, her chin elevated to almost painful levels, 'since I *am* tired, I think I'll have an early night and relieve you of my presence.' She stalked towards the stairs.

The dignity of her exit was slightly marred when, with one foot on the final step, she had to turn and ask, 'I assume I'm to use the blue room again?'

Despite her claim to be tired, she found she could not sleep. There was no physical reason for it. The room seemed to welcome her and the large four-poster bed enveloped her like loving arms, while her head sank into a pillow soft with goosefeathers. But still, hours after she had gone upstairs, she was awake and restless.

She knew why, of course. She was under the same roof as Ross Savage. But that was not close association enough. She wanted to be nearer. In the same room. In the same bed. By day it might be a little easier to control one's thoughts and bodily desires, but at night it was next to impossible, especially in the sybaritic luxury of this bed, which lent itself to sensual imaginings.

There was only one expedient she could think of. She must get up and take a cold shower, the colder the better.

She had disdained sleeping in the hated robe and now, naked, she slipped down from the bed and went into the bathroom. The vast bath would be a marvellous place in which to wallow on cold winters' nights, she thought. It was large enough for two and... Stop it! she adjured herself. You're making things worse.

She turned on the shower to its fullest extent, so that as well as the punishment of the cold water the drops stung her skin. She *would* drive out the devil of desire.

She was shivering when she stepped once more from beneath the jet and wrapped in the towel went back into the bedroom. Roughly she towelled herself until her skin glowed pink.

Allowing the towel to slide to the floor, she was just climbing back up into the high bed when she heard the door open behind her. With an undignified scramble she made it beneath the covers—but too late, she was aware.

'R-Ross?' she quavered, the duvet held up to her chin. 'Wh-what is it? What do you want? Is...is there news of Wanda?'

To her surprise he was only wearing a towel, just as if he too had come from the shower. It was a smaller towel than hers had been and it was wound sarong-style about his hips. Above the towel was a broad expanse of muscular chest, sun-bronzed and coated with those same fine hairs that had held her attention once before.

Below the towel... She swallowed, for its brevity did not leave much to the imagination. Below the towel there stretched an extraordinarily long length of leg, tanned too and considerably more hirsute than his chest, the hairs clinging damply to the flesh. He *had* just showered.

'No news of your cousin,' he said curtly, and then, 'You didn't lock your door after all?' It sounded like an accusation.

'I . . . I forgot,' she said truthfully. She'd had other things on her mind. 'Besides,' she couldn't resist adding, 'after what you said, I didn't think it would be necessary.'

'Perhaps it wouldn't have been, if I hadn't realised *you* were still awake too.' He gestured towards the open bathroom door. 'Our suites adjoin. For ease of plumbing the bathrooms are next door to each other. I was in the shower and heard yours running. It seemed strange, considering you claimed to be so tired, several hours ago.'

He came right into the room, closing the outer door behind him. 'Couldn't you sleep after all?'

'N-No,' she admitted. 'C-Couldn't you?'

'No.' He was pacing about the room in a fashion very reminiscent of a frustrated tiger.

Frustrated. The thought made her shiver. Was it possible that Ross had been experiencing the same thoughts and sensations as herself? Was that why he too had sought the shower cabinet? An involuntary contraction convulsed her stomach and, unseen beneath the duvet, she clenched her fists in an effort at self-control.

'Why couldn't *you* sleep, Claire?' he asked, unfairly, she thought.

'I . . . I suppose it was having too m-much excitement,' she said after a while, when she could stand his regular silent patrol no longer. And in case he should misunderstand, 'I mean, the...the flight and...and everything. T-Too much mental stimulation.'

He gave a harsh laugh and swung round to look at her. 'Is that *all* today stimulated in you, Claire? Is it?' He came closer to the bed, and she shrank back a little. He looked so formidable, almost like Joe at his most angry. She had to remind herself that he wasn't Joe and that he had no right to scold or intimidate her.

'Have you any idea what today has done to me?' he demanded, and when she did not answer, 'I've been thinking about your strange behaviour at dinner. I asked you if you were angry with me, and you said no. Did you mean that?'

She nodded, unable to meet his penetrating gaze.

'Then I can only conclude that I frightened you in some way. Is that it, Claire? Have your experiences with your erstwhile husband put you off any form of intimacy with a man?'

Claire sighed shudderingly. She spoke in a low voice. 'I...I thought they had. Until...until recently.'

'How recently?' he snapped, and as she did not answer, 'I said how recently, Claire? Is there another man, for instance, back home in England?' It was the way Joe might have asked the same question—jealously. But Ross couldn't be jealous, could he?

'No,' she mumbled. 'No, there's no one else.'

He was standing at the side of the bed now, directly above her. She could feel the warmth emanating from him, smell the spicy tang of his shower gel. Again she clenched her hands. It would take such a very small movement to reach out and touch him.

'Claire, look at me,' he commanded.

She couldn't. She knew her eyes were too full of what she was feeling right now. Her pride wouldn't let her be the first to reveal... But then what would his reveal? Love? Or just plain old-fashioned lust?

She knew the chances were that, if she gave him just the slightest hint of encouragement, he would make love to her here and now.

Did she want that? Yes, on one level she did. The most basic primitive level of all. Another less primordial instinct cried out for something more. She wanted to hear words, not just of bodily hunger, but of love, of commitment.

'Claire, I said look at me.' And when she still did not respond, he sat down on the side of the bed and turned her towards him, his hand beneath her chin in a now familiar gesture.

Green eyes locked with grey, and Claire caught her breath. His burned with an unmistakable intensity that sent little shock waves of sensation rippling through her. Shock waves that grew into tidal waves of insupportable desire.

'You said "until recently", Claire. Does that mean...?' His eyes completed the question and she felt colour run up under her fair skin, felt as though it flooded the whole of her body beneath the concealing duvet.

'Yes,' she whispered.

'Say it, Claire.' His grasp on her chin tightened. 'Tell me!'

'N-No, I c-can't. Not unless...' her expression pleaded with him '...y-you first.'

'But I've already told you, Claire.' Ross released her chin and now his hands cupped her face, his thumbs gentling, stroking, his eyes on her quivering mouth. 'This afternoon, up there in the balloon, I told you then. Nothing has changed since.'

His closeness, the touch of his hands, the tone of his voice, all were seducing her senses. But still she hesitated. 'I...I thought things had changed. You seemed to go so cold, so remote. I thought *you* were angry with *me*. You're...you're always so scathing about women—especially about the women who've pursued you. I thought that *you* thought...' She knew she was becoming incoherent.

'I wasn't angry with *you*.' He put an arm about her shoulders and pulled her against him, so that her head rested in the angle of his neck. 'If I was angry with anyone it was with those men, for vulgarising what I was feeling. I've seen too much of the vulgarisation of human relationships.'

Before she could ask him what he meant, he went on, 'And I was angry with myself as well, because I thought perhaps I'd been premature. I planned to wait—until you knew me better. Until I knew you didn't distrust and fear me as you'd learned to distrust and fear your husband. I didn't want to frighten you, Claire.'

'I wasn't frightened,' she said softly. 'When I first saw you, you did remind me a little of...of...' She faltered, wondering if he would be insulted.

'Of whom?' he said sharply, and he did sound tense and annoyed. But she had to be completely honest with him.

'Of my...my husband,' she said and was surprised when he did not burst into angry speech. Instead he seemed to relax. 'But I know now,' she went on hurriedly while she still had the chance, 'that it was only a fleeting physical resemblance, that you're not at all like him as a person.'

'So,' he enquired softly, 'now that we have all that out in the open, is it possible for you to say what you're feeling? Honestly and without fear?'

Claire reflected sadly that if she were to tell him, with total honesty, just what she was feeling, he would probably run a mile. She compromised. 'I . . . I want you too,' she whispered, so low that he had to bend his head to hear her. And then, shy and embarrassed, she buried her head against his chest so that he could not see her face.

Beneath her cheek she felt the rise and fall of his ribcage, the accelerated beating of his strong heart.

'Oh, God—*Claire*!' he murmured raggedly. Then his head bent and he forced hers up, claiming her mouth in a searching rather than a taking kiss. 'It doesn't seem possible that I've only known you a few days.' His mouth moved erotically against her throat, mouthing its hollows. 'But every night, since the first day I met you, I've thought of you, wanted you. I couldn't believe it—your effect on me.'

Once more his lips plundered hers, then, 'To start with, I fought against it. God, *how* I fought! I told myself I'd seen too much, learned too much of women, their greed, their lies. It wasn't *me* they wanted but what I represented to them, to the world. They wanted me not out of love, but as a status symbol, a scalp worth having on their belts. Claire, they almost emasculated me. Can you understand that?'

'Yes,' she told him softly, compassionately. She could understand. Joe's brutal use of her, his claustrophobic possessiveness, had struck at the roots of her femininity. She too had almost been destroyed.

Almost, but not quite. This man had given her back what she had thought lost. Surely she could do no less for him?

His mouth claimed hers again and he crushed her against the hardness of his chest.

Already weakened by fatigue, Claire felt unable to combat the waves of desire that washed her in their dangerous tide. She wanted Ross. And if she was as honest as he, she would admit that it had been the same for her as for him. *She* hadn't been able to get *him* out of her mind ever since they'd met.

They had both been repressing the physicality that obsessed them, a physicality that might have exploded at any moment in the last few days. But that moment was here, now.

She realised that Ross was searching her face, his grey eyes questioning. And she knew she could no longer withhold the answer to that question.

'I want you, Ross,' she said again, and held out her arms to him.

'Dear God—oh, dear God,' he muttered. His hand caressed the smooth bare skin of her shoulders, then moved slowly down, stroking, then cupping one small firm breast, his thumb discovering its central nub, already peaked with desire. His breath caught in his throat on a jagged sound. 'Claire, does that mean...are you going to let me...? You said no "relationships", but you won't send me away? Not now?'

If she had any sense she knew she would. Because, once she had given herself physically to this man, for her at least there would be no going back. She would be his, for evermore. And though he'd admitted to wanting her, she could not be sure that he would ever feel the same commitment. A man who liked to live alone, who valued his personal privacy, might be satisfied with a periodic succession of love-affairs.

'Ross, I . . . I . . .'

'Claire . . .' At the note of doubt in her voice his became softly coaxing. 'Darling, this isn't wrong, and I want you so much, so very much.'

He was drawing the duvet down now, and her body had no secrets from him as he worshipped it with his eyes and with his hands, moving them over the pale silky skin that no amount of sun could ever successfully brown.

'Did you know,' he said wonderingly, 'that you have the most attractive cluster of freckles on your midriff?' He bent his head and planted a series of feather-light kisses on her skin as though he intended to bestow a kiss on every separate freckle. The touch of his lips was exquisite torture, and she gasped, plunging her hands into the thickness of his hair, not with any intention of restraining his advances, but rather to keep him a prisoner there.

His lips moved lower then and with slow serpent-like darts his tongue explored the hollow of her navel, while his hands embarked upon more daring and intimate explorations.

'Oh, Ross!' His name was dragged from her lips— the groan of a woman driven almost beyond endurance. She reached out for him, and as she did so he unwound the towel from about his waist and in one lithe movement he slid the whole length of his body on to the bed beside her, moist flesh against moist flesh, the rough hair of his chest brushing erotically against the hardened tips of her breasts.

He crushed her to him in a powerful spasm of eroticism, leaving her in no doubt of the ferocity of his own desires.

He relaxed slightly as she began to plant little kisses against his sweat-slicked shoulder—but not for long. As her hands explored the hard lines of his body she felt him shudder and knew that he was fast approaching the point where nothing mattered but their wild caresses, the increasing sensuality of their kisses.

'Claire?' He groaned her name, drawing her on top of him. 'I meant to be so gentle with you, to make these moments long and memorable... But I...I need you...now...'

'It's all right, Ross,' she whispered. 'It's *all right*.'

He rolled over, pinning her to the bed beneath him as with tongue and teeth he tormented the throbbing peaks of her breasts.

'Now, Ross,' she begged. 'Oh, now, *please*!'

And then he possessed her, filled her aching cavity with himself, moving deeply into her in long throbbing thrusts that sent waves of almost unbearable delight surging through her. With a little cry she wrapped her legs about him, meeting and matching each thrust.

As the heat of passion engulfed and shook her body, with a ragged groan he reached his own summit and they shuddered into mutual fulfilment.

'Claire, oh, Claire!' he marvelled, burying his face against her breasts, his arms still tight about her.

His breathing was slow to steady, and when it did he was silent for so long that she thought he must have fallen asleep, and a sense of outrage possessed her. Dark memories came to haunt her, memories of Joe, who, after his violent possessions of her, had always fallen into a heavy, sluggish slumber with no thought for her comfort or feelings.

But she had misjudged Ross. 'Was that as wonderful for you as it was for me?' he murmured, and the evil shadow was dispelled.

'Yes,' she told him rapturously. 'Oh, yes!'

He moved to lean on his elbow, looking down at her. With his hair ruffled he looked a younger, more vulnerable man than the one from whom she'd run on that first day. 'You're mine now,' he said. And then, urgently, 'You'll stay, Claire? You won't ever go away?'

Sudden panic possessed her and she avoided his gaze. In what capacity was he asking her to stay? And he misread the cause of her fear.

'Don't look so alarmed. I know you said you'd never remarry, and I respect your reasons for that. Your marriage was a trap—and I've known another kind of entrapment. But there's no reason why we shouldn't be lovers.'

Her fears realised, she asked, 'For...for how long?'

'For as long as you're happy with me, my darling. But I hope there won't ever be any need for you to go away.'

He didn't seem to notice that she hadn't replied as once more he took her mouth by storm.

This time their coming together was slower, longer, but no less intense. And this time they both fell asleep.

Dawn was just breaking when Claire was awoken by Ross's hands and mouth upon her breasts.

'I can't seem to get enough of you,' he confessed as she turned drowsily into his arms. 'When I first woke up I was afraid for a moment that it had all been a dream. And then I turned over and you were there and I . . . You won't leave me, will you, Claire?'

'I won't leave,' she said. How could she join that band of women who had hurt and disillusioned him?

So why, when to stay was what *she* wanted too, did a cold chill of premonition run through her, even as he claimed her for the third time?

CHAPTER SEVEN

THE sun was high in the sky when they woke again.

'Heavens!' Claire exclaimed. 'If Wanda did get back last night she'll be wondering what on earth's become of me.'

'And where do you think you're going?' Ross protested as she began to roll out of bed.

'I must get showered and dressed and go down to the field.'

'Oh, no, you don't!' Steely fingers captured her leg and restrained her. 'Not yet, anyway. Not until you've had some breakfast. Your cousin had no concern for *your* anxieties, so she can just wait a little longer. In any case, I should think she'll have a pretty good idea where you are. As to that shower you mentioned,' he added with a wicked grin, 'it's a cliché, but true, that a pleasure shared is a pleasure doubled.'

It was some considerable time before they made their way downstairs to breakfast.

'*Bonjour, monsieur, mademoiselle.* I trust you had a good night?'

Despite her own claim to mastery of the language, the Frenchwoman's English was sometimes a little ambiguous, and Claire found herself blushing as Madame Pierrepointe served their coffee and hot croissants. So late were they in breakfasting and so conscious was she of what had taken place last night between herself and Ross that she felt it must be blazoned in their faces for the housekeeper to see.

'I don't think either of us have anything to complain about, *madame*,' Ross told her with a deadpan expression which nearly sent Claire off into a fit of the giggles.

She managed to master herself sufficiently to thank the housekeeper for the laundering of her clothes. She would be glad, though, when she could discard yesterday's jeans and blouse for something more feminine.

Later, on her own, she fell into a more sober mood. She had expected difficulty in persuading Ross to let her go down to the camping site on her own. But he seemed satisfied by her explanation that she would be embarrassed by his presence when she told her cousin that she planned to stay on at the Moulin Gris.

'And I have to change,' she told him.

'OK, but just hurry back,' he adjured her. Then, halting her on the threshold, 'Claire, you don't regret what happened between us last night?'

She looked up at him. *Did* she regret it? Regret giving herself to a man who had shown her tenderness and giving rather than just possessiveness? No, she couldn't regret last night. Her only fear was that she would become physically and emotionally dependent on Ross and that some day she might get hurt.

'Claire?' he pressed, and she realised she had been silent, considering his question for an unflattering length of time.

'No, Ross, I don't regret it. But——'

'That's good.' He didn't give her a chance to go on, to put her fear into words. Instead he possessed her mouth softly, his hand on her spine moulding her to him. And of their own volition her arms went up about his neck, her lips parting fully so that he might deepen the kiss. 'Hurry back,' he said again as, reluctantly, he released her.

Their relationship might not be completely satisfactory from her point of view, Claire thought as she hurried down the lane, but it was nice to know that Ross was as eager for her company as she for his.

And after all, she argued against the uneasy inner voice, who would she be hurting by living with Ross as his lover? She refused to think of herself as his 'mistress'. That word had incurred too much disrepute in the past.

She would be hurting no one. She had no parents to object. And while her aunt Alice might not approve, Claire did not anticipate any criticism from Wanda.

Ross was right, she tried to convince herself. With no legal strings neither of them need feel trapped in the relationship. Instead each could respect the other's essential freedom.

Her absence from the Moulin Gris was shorter even than Ross could have hoped for. The moment she came in sight of the field, Claire realised the caravan was still not there.

Last night, in Ross's arms, all misgivings about her cousin's safety had been swept away. And this morning she had been so sure Wanda would have returned. Now all her fears came back to haunt her, and she hurried back to the old mill, bursting in on Ross at his daily colloquy with Madame Pierrepointe.

'Ross! Oh, Ross, she's not there. Something's wrong—I know it is. Wanda wouldn't leave me stranded overnight like that unless something had happened to her!'

'Calm down, calm down.' His arm encircled her comfortingly. 'Let's not meet trouble halfway, eh?

We'll have an early lunch and then I'll get the car and we'll see if we can pick up your cousin's trail. We should try Cadenet first, don't you think?'

Claire nodded dumbly. She had to know if her cousin was safe, even if it meant bringing about the encounter Wanda had so far avoided.

She sat in anxious silence beside Ross as the Citroën negotiated the winding country lanes between Puit de Mirabeau and Cadenet.

He put a hand on her knee. 'Relax! You're as taut as a bowstring. There's probably some perfectly simple explanation.'

She smiled her gratitude, covering his hand briefly with her own. 'Thank goodness I've got you to help me. If I'd been all alone——'

'You'd have coped,' he said with certainty. 'That's another thing I like about you; you're not the fluttering helpless type.' His mouth drew downwards in a grimace. 'How I hate the dim-witted type of female who pulls that "me little Jane, you he-man Tarzan" act!'

Despite her concern for Wanda, Claire could not repress a giggle. But her mirth did not dispel Ross's frown.

'You can laugh, but if you'd seen some of the god-awful females that used to pursue me—to my own front door, some of them. And beyond,' he concluded grimly.

Claire eyed him speculatively. Now that her immediate future at least was linked with Ross's, would he enlighten her about his past?

'You talk about those women as if...well, as if they were women in the plural,' she ventured, 'as though they descended on you in hordes.'

'Some of them did,' he agreed drily. 'But there was the occasional lone huntress too. And they were the most dangerous.'

'Why——?' she began, but he interrupted.

'Look, that's Cadenet up ahead. And there's a local gendarme. Might be worth asking if he knows of any mishap to a motor-caravan around here.'

The policeman, though anxious to help, could tell them nothing. And a drive through the streets of Cadenet brought no sightings of their quarry.

'You said your cousin and her friend usually go into Aix?' Ross said. 'Perhaps we should try there. It'll be a bit like looking for a needle in a haystack, but at least we could enquire at the *gendarmerie* if there have been any accidents reported.'

'It's putting you to an awful lot of trouble,' Claire demurred.

He angled her a smile. 'Nothing is too much trouble for you, my dear Claire. And besides...' the smile became a suggestive grin, his words making her blush, '...the next time you're in my arms—which I hope will be very soon—I want your mind concentrated on *me* and not on missing cousins!'

Their route to Aix followed a corkscrew road through the mountains, with nothing to see but the steep and empty landscape of grey rock and green scrub oak. Nothing to distract Claire from a subject always at the back of her mind.

'You started to tell me about those women who used to chase you. That robe I wore last night—did that belong to one of them?'

Ross could not take his attention from the winding road, but Claire, watching him, witnessed his sudden frown. 'I hope I don't detect a note of jealousy,' he said. But she was spared the necessity of an indignant—and untruthful—denial as he went on, 'That robe, and incidentally the riding clothes, belong to Madeleine St Cloud. Maddy's a keen horsewoman and she and her husband stay with me from time to time. You'll meet her and Raoul soon. I'm giving a dinner party for a few close friends.'

'Oh?' Claire said doubtfully. Her role in Ross's life was too new for her to feel confident at the prospect of meeting his intimates. For a start, how and as what would he introduce her?

Ross seemed unaware of her misgivings. 'I'd like you to act as my hostess for the occasion. In the past Madeleine has——'

'Oh, no, Ross!' At least here was a qualm Claire could give voice to. 'I wouldn't like Madame St Cloud to be——'

'Nonsense, Maddy won't mind a bit.'

'And I haven't anything suitable to wear. You don't pack evening dress for a caravan holiday.'

'Then we'll go shopping in Aix——'

'We're going to Aix to make enquiries about Wanda,' she reminded him a little sharply. It didn't seem right to be making plans to enjoy herself when her cousin might be in a hospital bed—or worse— right at this very moment.

'That won't take all day tomorrow,' Ross said reasonably.

'*Tomorrow?*'

'You didn't think we could make the trip, pursue our enquiries and get back to Puit de Mirabeau all in one day? It will be almost evening when we arrive. Naturally we shall stay overnight.'

'But . . . but we didn't bring any——'

'Surely all *we* need, my love, is a toothbrush apiece?' His smile left her in no doubt of what he was suggesting.

'Oh!' Claire felt the heat from her blush extending to the whole of her body.

'Since I hope,' Ross went with a quick mischievous glance at her, 'that you won't be insisting on separate rooms.'

'And if I don't?' she challenged him, her voice suddenly brittle at the thought of the invidious position in which she had placed herself, 'how will you sign the hotel register?'

'No need for a hotel,' he said smugly, 'I have friends in Aix who'll be delighted to accommodate us.'

'And how will you describe me to *them*?' Claire couldn't seem to drop the subject even though she suspected she would not like the answer.

Ross shot her a thoughtful look. 'How would you *like* to be described?'

As your fiancé, she thought miserably, soon to be your wife. Aloud, she said, 'Do I have a choice? There aren't that many ways of putting it, are there?'

'Oh, I don't know.' He sounded amused, damn him. 'But since we don't have a thesaurus between us, may I suggest—since we're in France—that we use the French term *petite amie*? An unexceptionally inoffensive way of describing it, don't you think?'

Claire could only mumble some kind of agreement, and she fell silent now as they left the foothills of the Luberon behind and headed south on the Nationale Sept.

It was another scorchingly hot day, and Claire felt far too warm in the jeans she had worn for the balloon ascent. The heat made her doze off, and when she woke they were entering Aix via a handsome main street lined by plane trees that formed a pale green tunnel some five hundred yards long.

'Wake up, sleepyhead,' Ross said affectionately. 'We'll go straight to my friends' house,' he decided, 'and arrange for our overnight stay. Then, after dinner, we'll go down to the *gendarmerie*.'

Claire had expected Ross's friends to be another married couple. But Pierre Bonnard and Marie Clément were brother and sister, Pierre about Ross's age, his sister, a widow, considerably older. They did not seem to find it at all strange that Ross should arrive with a female companion, nor a matter for disapproval that they wished to share a room.

Had Ross brought other women here? she couldn't help wondering, and her manner with him was a little stiff when they were left alone to freshen up after their long drive.

'Still feeling embarrassed?' Ross asked, coming up behind her as she stared unseeingly through the window into the street below. 'There's no need. Marie and Pierre have never been hidebound by convention.' His hands caressed the length of her arms as he held her back against him. But for once Claire was not weakened by his proximity.

'And I suppose they're quite accustomed to you arriving with your *petite amie* of the moment,' she snapped.

His hands clamped down hard, but she resisted as he tried to turn her towards him. 'Claire, what *is* all this?' he demanded. 'Why are you talking such nonsense? Are you just tired after the journey? Because, if so——'

'No!' Dreading that he might suggest bed as a remedy, she denied fatigue, though in truth last night's wakefulness and then today's anxieties *had* taken their toll of her strength.

'Then what it it? I know you're concerned for your cousin, but we'll shortly be doing what we can to allay your fears. So why take it out on me?' And now he did succeed in jerking her round to face him.

'I'm not,' she said. 'Oh, I am worried about Wanda, but it's not that.'

He looked down at her with steady, stern grey eyes. 'Then I think you'd better explain yourself. And keep it simple and honest. Kindly don't play me a dramatic scene.'

Claire's shoulders slumped suddenly. 'All right,' she said tonelessly, 'I suppose I've made it pretty obvious that I didn't . . . don't like the idea that maybe you've brought other women here—in similar circumstances. But—well——'

'Claire!' he interrupted her harshly, 'let's get one thing straight, shall we? I've known you for just one week, right? You told me you're twenty-six. I know for a fact that you've been married. Maybe before that there were other men in your life. But it would be unreasonable of me to resent those men, to make jealous scenes over them. It's equally unreasonable of you to resent and question *my* past.'

He was right, of course, she thought with guilty misery. She'd suffered enough in the past from jealous possessiveness, enough to have known better. But jealousy was an emotion she had never experienced until recently, and now she realised just how much it could hurt.

'I don't have to tell you this,' Ross went on grimly, 'but in the past few years there haven't been any women in my life. Friends, yes, the wives of my men friends, but no *petites amies*. And let me tell you here and now,' he continued, 'one of the chief reasons I've avoided women like the plague in these last few years is their jealous, unreasonable scenes. I thought, in view of the unhappy incidents during your marriage, you'd be different.'

'Ross,' she began, I——' but he swept on inexorably.

'If you can't cope with our relationship, if you want to end it here and now, say so. But make it a clean break, will you? No pettiness, no tantrums.' He turned his back on her and walked towards the door.

'Ross!' Claire cried, her heart in her mouth. 'Please, I——'

'Oh, don't worry,' he threw over his shoulder, 'I'll still help you look for your cousin.'

Another moment and it would be too late. He would be out of the bedroom and her chance to make amends would be lost. She ran across the room and interposed herself between him and the door.

'Ross, please don't go. I'm sorry. And you're right—I've no business being jealous of your past. I guess I *am* tired and it's making me unreasonable.' Her voice faltered. 'And . . . and I don't want to end our . . . our . . .'

At once she was swept up into strong arms, held tightly against Ross's chest as he kissed her with hungry thoroughness. 'I don't want it to end either, Claire,' he said huskily.

And then everything was forgotten except kissing him back, melting against him as though she would become a part of him. She loved him, and that was all that really mattered.

'I want you, Claire,' he murmured after a while. 'I want you . . . now.'

She made only a half-hearted protest as he carried her towards the bed, as his hand moved into the V-neckline of her blouse to curve possessively about her breast. She pulled his head down, green eyes almost drowning in the depth of grey before their mouths moved over each other once again in rising passion.

'I want you too,' she told him softly.

'Do you?' he said against her ear, his teeth worrying the lobe.

'You know I do,' she groaned.

'And we'll forget the past, Claire?' he asked huskily. 'It's dead and gone. The present is what matters, isn't it? You and me.'

'Yes.' Claire gave herself up to the inevitable. She was his, for as long or short a time as he wanted her. And right now she knew he wanted her very much. 'But . . . but won't your friends wonder——?'

'Let them wonder!' he growled.

Pleasure swamped her, and she squirmed against him with sensual abandon as he brushed aside the material of her blouse and claimed one throbbing breast with moist lips, nibbling at the soft flesh with mounting eroticism.

Then her jeans and blouse were discarded, her underclothes swiftly following. Impatiently he threw his own clothes to the floor and joined her on the bed.

She ran her hand up his leg and along his hardening thigh, gasping a little as she discovered the extent of his arousal. Somehow their disagreement had heated their hunger for each other, and they came together in an explosion of sensation that left them panting and exhausted.

Ross's head lay against her breasts and he caressed her still-shuddering body. 'Don't ever fight with me again, Claire,' he whispered throatily, 'or at least, if you do, always let it end like this. For a moment there, I thought it was all over between us.'

'Would you have been sorry?' Secure in his need of her, her whole body one mass of pleasurable sensation, she teased him languorously.

As she looked into his eyes, she saw desire already rekindling. 'More sorry than I can tell you,' he said with husky sincerity.

'I'm not usually a jealous person,' she assured him against the hard warmth of his chest. 'You're right, I know only too well what it's like to be the object of jealousy. I don't know why...' She broke off and then, with determined honesty, 'Yes, I do know. I was suddenly afraid. You see, I'm not quite sure what you want of me, where we're going. I swore not to get involved again—at least, not so soon. And yet here I am...' She broke off again, not daring to add what was in her thoughts—fathoms deep in love.

'We're lovers, my darling.' Possessively Ross trailed his lips over her breasts, his hands making intimate forays. 'And all I want is you. I won't demand anything you don't want to give.'

And she, by that token, Claire thought, must not make demands on him that he could not fulfil, such as permanence, commitment. She drew a deep steadying breath, the better to make her words sound convincing.

'And *I* won't ask *you* for what you can't give,' she told him, 'and I suppose fidelity——'

'Hold on! Hold on!' He gripped her tightly. 'There's no question of my being unfaithful to you.

For as long as you want me, I intend to spend every night in *your* arms. And I hope you can say the same?'

'Oh, yes, oh, yes, Ross.' It was permanence of a kind. It *could* last a lifetime—as long as any marriage. Certainly *she* would not be the first to cry hold. She put her arms about him and soon passion, once more out of control, flared between them.

They slept deeply in each other's arms, and Claire woke at last with a start of surprise to find Ross shaking her.

'It seems a shame to disturb you,' he said, 'but I really think we should show ourselves at the dinner table, don't you?'

'I apologise for not changing,' Claire told her host and hostess as they sat down to dine, 'but I only have what I stand up in. My cousin's disappeared with our caravan—and all my clothes.'

Madame Clément merely smiled an acknowledgement, but her brother's English was more fluent.

'No need to apologise. *You* would look charming whatever you wore. You are a very beautiful woman, *ma chère.*' And Claire surprised a flicker of something in Ross's grey eyes. After all his strictures about jealousy, she gloated, Ross did not like Pierre Bonnard's outspoken admiration of her.

She did not set out deliberately to flirt with Pierre. But he was an attractive extrovert, a sparkling conversationalist, and she could not help expanding under the warmth of his bold-eyed approval. Over dinner they chatted like old friends, leaving Madame Clément and Ross to entertain each other.

Pierre quizzed Claire about her hobbies, and waxed enthusiastic about his own. 'My obsession is with my conservatory,' he told her over the excellent coffee. 'I cultivate many rare plants. Our hobbies could be combined, *ma chère Claire*. You could photograph my specimens. Perhaps you would care to see them?'

'Claire!' Ross interrupted without ceremony, pushing back his chair and standing up. 'Have you forgotten why we're in Aix?' he demanded curtly. 'There's no time for viewing Pierre's conservatory. We have to visit the *gendarmerie*. Unless,' sarcastically, 'you would prefer to stay here while *I* go?'

Hastily she drained her cup. 'No, of course not—I'm coming.' And to Pierre, apologetically, 'Perhaps you could show me your plants tomorrow?'

They left Pierre Bonnard's house in the *crépuscule*, the French word that Claire always felt made twilight sound like a skin complaint, and the street cafés were ablaze with lights.

Ross seemed to have nothing to say as he strode along, Claire almost running to keep up with him.

At the *gendarmerie* it was Ross who took charge, rattling out his questions far too fast for Claire to follow despite her own excellent French.

'There's nothing known about an accident,' Ross translated for her. 'And any such happening between Cadenet and Aix *would* have been reported here. But they've promised to make more widespread enquiries overnight. I'll leave Pierre's number, but we'll come back in the morning anyway.'

It was an anticlimax. Claire had been building on her hopes of finding news of Wanda. To add to the bleakness of her feelings, Ross still seemed withdrawn as they made their way back at a slower pace. After a while Claire, as so often happened when she did not understand Ross's mood, tried to make conversation.

'Marie and Pierre seem very nice.'

'Yes. I noticed you liked them.'

She tried again. 'It's very good of them to put us up at such short notice.' And since this did not really require any response, she went on, 'Will *they* be coming to your party?'

They had regained the house now, and Ross paused infinitesimally on the threshold, an overhead light throwing his features into strong relief.

'You'd like that, would you?'

Claire, unaware of the verbal trap, responded cheerfully as she followed him inside, 'Oh, yes. At least I'd know them.'

'You mean you'd know *Pierre*,' he grated.

She stared up at him, into glittering grey eyes. 'Ross, what do you mean? I don't . . .' And then, 'Oh, yes, I *do* understand.' She gave a short bitter laugh. 'Oh, this is ironic! At dinner I thought for a moment . . . But then I told myself, no, not Ross, not after all he's said. But you *were*, weren't you? You *are*! You're jealous—you hypocrite! You're just like Joe after all!' And, brushing by his outstretched hand, she fled upstairs.

At first she thought the banging noise was the reverberation of the bedroom door closing behind her. But a glance through the window showed her Ross striding away from the house into the night.

What had she expected? That he would come after her? Prolong the confrontation? No, Joe would have done, but that was not Ross's way. In anger he withdrew into himself.

If this had been her own house, or even Ross's house, she could have locked the bedroom door against his return. But she could not cause a scene in someone else's home, nor embarrass Ross in front of his friends.

It was a little early to go to bed. But to go downstairs would lead to awkward questions about Ross's whereabouts. And besides, if he came back and found her chatting to Pierre Bonnard...

Clad only in her flimsy underwear, Claire climbed into the huge double bed.

She couldn't sleep. It was hot, even under the single layer of sheet that covered her, and, after the peace of the Moulin Gris, the town noises seemed exaggerated. The old house creaked and groaned so that several times she started, thinking she heard footsteps approaching the bedroom door. Would Ross come back before morning? And if he did, would he still share this bed?

The traffic noises had long ceased and she was finally drifting into unconsciousness when the bedroom door opened. At once she was wide awake and tense. But she remained still, feigning sleep.

She listened to the movements, the rustling sounds that told her Ross was discarding his clothes. She knew the exact moment when he slid beneath the sheet.

The size of the bed meant that a vast gulf separated them. It would take more than a slight accidental movement to bridge that gap. She *wouldn't* be the first to speak, she resolved. Ross had been totally unreasonable, angry with her one moment for giving way to jealousy and the next moment displaying the selfsame emotion.

'Claire?' His deep voice, unexpected in the silent room, made her jump betrayingly. 'Claire, I know you're awake. Can we talk?'

'I suppose so,' she said in a grudging tone of voice. But in reality she wanted nothing more than to have the air cleared between them. Her body ached for his touch and his lovemaking.

He flicked on the overhead light, and as she turned to face him, she found him sitting bolt upright, in profile to her, his arms folded tightly across his strong chest.

'I've been walking,' he said, his tone brittle. 'I couldn't trust myself near you until I had myself under control again.'

At his words Claire drew in a sharp breath. Surely he hadn't been on the verge of violence? Not Ross. Oh, please, not Ross too, she prayed. Was it something in *her* that brought out the darker side of men's natures?

'It's all right, Claire,' he answered her unspoken thought. 'You were never in any danger that way. I've told you, I don't go in for beating women. Besides, my anger was against myself.'

'Then why did you have to——?'

'Because I needed some thinking time, time to rationalise my own inconsistent behaviour. I can tell you, Claire, I read myself a pretty stiff lecture out there.'

He was silent then, and Claire, left in a state of suspense, began to find the silence intolerable.

'And what was the outcome of your thinking, your lecture?' she asked.

He turned to look at her then, and something in his face and in the slight movement of his body made her think for a moment that he was going to take her in his arms.

But no. He seemed to have himself under some tight restraint. 'Before I tell you that,' he said slowly, 'we have to go further back. I asked you to stay with me, Claire, but since then I've realised——'

'Yes?' Claire felt her stomach turn over and despite the hot sultry night she felt a chill possess her limbs. Was he going to say he'd changed his mind? Her voice shook as she urged, 'And since then?'

'I've realised that I was asking you to take me very much on trust. I've grown so accustomed to keeping myself apart, guarding my privacy, that it's become second nature to be secretive. I owe it to you to tell you something of my past. The reason why I . . . And then leave it to you to decide whether you still want to stay.'

His voice sounded so bleak that she edged closer to him and put a tentative hand on his arm.

'Surely your past can't be *that* black?' she said gently. 'I can't believe you're going to tell me anything bad enough to drive me away.'

He covered her fingers with his own. 'Bless you, Claire.' And then, removing her hand and placing it firmly on her lap, 'But don't distract me. I'm finding it hard enough to resist you as it is. But I'm not going to make love to you until you know . . . well, until you know something of my story.'

Which sounded, Claire thought, as though he still intended to reserve some details to himself.

'Until five years ago,' Ross said, 'as you may have gathered, I was pretty much in the public eye, for . . . for one cause or another. And I collected a following— quite unsolicited, I hasten to add—of women, who for some reason known only to themselves saw me as their ideal.'

She could quite understand why women should idolise him. But Ross obviously wanted her to keep her own counsel and listen.

'It began innocently enough—letters, requests for signed photographs. But as my public image grew so did the demands. I received proposals of marriage, flowers, extravagant gifts and...and other not so pleasant tokens of their devotion.'

'Such as?' Diverted, Claire could not resist asking.

'Women,' he said flatly, 'sent me items of...of clothing. Underclothing.'

As the colour ran up under his tan she had to hide a smile. For a man who could be so passionately sensual and uninhibited, she thought, he was also quite surprisingly strait-laced.

'Then, even though I didn't advertise my whereabouts, they started arriving on my doorstep. In groups. In ones and twos. And occasionally a single woman would turn up.' His mouth tightened and there was an expression in his eyes that Claire could not at first fathom. But as he went on, she realised it was one of horror, that he was haunted by some 'might have been'.

'The house I owned in England had a very high wall around it—I bought it for that reason. The previous owner was a pop star. *He'd* had the wall reinforced with spiked railings. I *had* meant to do something about those railings, but somehow I never got around to it.'

'There was an accident?' Claire surmised.

'Yes. One of those "lone huntresses" came close to killing herself. God knows how she didn't spike herself. As it was, she ended up with a broken ankle and some very nasty bruises. But when I think what might have happened...' he shuddered, '...just in a fit of hysterical hero-worship. That was when I decided to move abroad. I just didn't want the responsibility for any more accidents.'

'But it wasn't *your* fault,' Claire said comfortingly. 'Because some stupid autograph-hunter...'

'It was more than my signature they were after.' And, in tones of outrage, 'Do you know what they *did* want?'

Now Claire could not repress a smile. 'Well,' she said provocatively, 'if they found you as irresistible as I do...' She let her words hang suggestively in the air, but her expressive eyes completed the sentence for her.

Again he made that abrupt movement as if towards her, and again restrained himself. But at least a faint smile softened his features.

'Minx! What *they* wanted was for me to kiss them. Oh, maybe some of them thought it would lead to other things. Certainly one shameless hoyden actually managed to get herself into the house and into my bed.'

'And *did* you kiss any of them?' Claire wanted to know. But she kept her tone light in case he should think she was giving way to jealousy again.

'No, I did not! I'd had enough of that sort of thing before I...before I sought obscurity. It was that which finally decided me to move abroad, and so far I've succeeded in preserving my anonymity.'

'So that's why you were so worried when you thought I was a reporter! You thought you'd been tracked down.'

'Exactly. But that's not all the story. You asked me once if I'd ever been married.'

'You said no,' she reminded him warningly.

'And it was true.' Almost absently, she thought, his arm went about her shoulders. 'But I came close to it a couple of times.'

Casually, in case he should notice what she was doing and order her away again, Claire nestled closer. 'What happened?' she asked.

'My first fiancée and I were very much in love. She was a quiet, gentle and intelligent girl. But she was also a very private person, and she hated all the fuss and commotion that followed me. In the end she just couldn't take it. She broke off our engagement. I don't mind telling you, I was pretty shattered by that. It was a long time before I picked up the pieces.'

The knowledge that he had once loved another woman—and so much—stabbed painfully through Claire, but gamely she fought the pain.

'And the other one?' she asked.

'*She*, luckily, was no loss. I discovered that she wasn't in love with me for myself. *She* wanted the fame, the public attention in order to further her own career. *I* ended that relationship. Do you wonder,' he asked bitterly, 'that I decided to get away from it all, to shun all forms of publicity?'

Claire sighed. 'No. And I understand now why you don't want any permanent commitment. I suppose you could never really be sure——'

'But that's in the past,' Ross interrupted her. He'd noticed her little manoeuvre all right, and far from objecting he was taking advantage of it, his hand smoothing and caressing the velvety skin of her arm, moving to take possession of a breast, shaping its nipple between finger and thumb, making her shiver sensuously. 'That's all in the past,' he said again, only this time it was murmured against her temple as his lips too began to explore. 'That's one of the things I realised tonight as I walked the streets of Aix. It's worked. I've made a life here for myself in Provence. It's years since any importunate female made her way to my door.'

'Except me,' Claire said demurely.

'Except you, my love,' he agreed. 'And you didn't know who I was. You had no ulterior motive.' Fleetingly his mouth brushed hers and eagerly she parted her lips, wanting him to deepen the kiss. But it seemed the talking was not yet over.

'Claire, I've a confession to make. I've misled you.'

Her heart missed a beat. 'How——? Why——? What——?' she stammered.

'From the best of intentions, I assure you. I've known you so short a time, and I didn't want to frighten you away. I knew you'd only just ended an unhappy marriage, that you weren't ready to enter into another one. So I let you think I felt the same way.'

'And...and you don't?' she said breathlessly, hardly daring to believe what he seemed to be saying.

'I don't. Oh, I was prepared to keep up the pretence for a while, to give you time. But that gave me no rights, no rights at all, and tonight, when I saw you with Pierre and then saw my own behaviour...well, I didn't like what I saw. And I knew I had to lay my cards on the table. Claire, I can't settle for anything less than marriage. Could you...? Will you...?'

'Yes, Ross,' she said with quiet sincerity. 'Oh, yes!'

'You *mean* that? Really mean it?' he demanded incredulously, but already the light of conviction—and of desire—was in his eyes.

'I really mean it. It's what I've wanted all along. But I thought *you* didn't——'

'What fools we've been!' Ross exclaimed as he swept her into his arms. 'When I think of the time we've wasted, fencing around——'

'Oh, I wouldn't say it had been entirely wasted,' Claire told him mischievously. 'There was last night— and this evening... Oh, Ross!' She was discovering that when he'd undressed he had shed his clothing in its entirety, and she was not allowed to retain her own modest scraps for long.

'If you think *that* was time well spent,' Ross growled playfully, 'you ain't seen nuthin' yet!'

CHAPTER EIGHT

'Well, that's a weight off my mind!' Claire exclaimed as they left the *gendarmerie* next morning. 'It seems almost certain there hasn't been an accident.'

'Yes,' Ross agreed. 'Personally, I'm inclined to think your precious cousin has just gone off about her own affairs—literally.'

'Maybe,' Claire conceded. 'But what now?'

'Shopping,' he reminded her. 'An evening dress. And, I would suggest, a few other items. Since all your clothes are in the caravan and we don't know when your cousin is going to show up.'

Claire shook her head, 'I suddenly realised, I can't go shopping. All my money, my traveller's cheques, my cheque-book and credit cards are in the caravan. I didn't take them ballooning with me.'

'No problem,' Ross said cheerfully. 'My treat.'

'Oh, no, I couldn't let you. I——'

'Why not? I take it that when we're married you won't have any objection to my buying your clothes. The fact that we're not married yet is only a technicality.' And purposefully he steered her towards the narrow streets that ran behind the main Cours, where most of the boutiques were to be found.

It did not take long to find a dress she liked. In fact Claire was spoiled for choice. But Ross was less easily pleased, insisting that she try on the full range that the chosen boutique had to offer and model them for his benefit. The modiste was flattering about "*mademoiselle's* exquisite face and figure", and Claire felt the skin of her face and neck burning as Ross's expressive eyes reinforced and enlarged on the woman's compliments.

'That's the one!' he said positively as she turned before him. 'The green is exactly the same as your eyes. And,' he seemed to find it necessary to clear his throat, 'it fits as though it were made for you.'

That was the understatement of the year, Claire thought as doubtfully she surveyed herself in the full-length mirror. The dress *was* lovely. It *did* enhance her vivid colouring. But it also left very little to the imagination, with its figure-hugging lines and plunging neckline.

Ross, however, was not to be dissuaded. 'That's the one!' he persisted. 'Because it makes you look every bit as desirable as you are,' he murmured against her ear as the modiste disappeared in search of wrappings. 'In fact, even better than seeing you wearing it is the thought of myself taking it off.' And his hand slid around her waist and upward, cupping her breast, an intimate gesture that sent her senses flaring.

'Ross!' she protested, half laughingly, half in earnest. 'Please, not here. She'll be back at any moment.'

Obediently he desisted, but, 'One thing I've learned about France and the French,' he told her, 'is that everyone loves a lover.'

By the time he was satisfied that she had purchased sufficient clothes for every eventuality, it was well after midday, and Claire admitted that she was hungry.

Aix being a university town, all the eating places were full of students, spilling over on to the sunny sidewalks. Ross managed, nevertheless, to find them a table at a small café in the Rue Frédéric Mistral.

'I'm still worried about Wanda,' Claire confessed as they ate. 'There are other things besides accidents that could have happened. This man she met—I know nothing about him. And she can't know all that much. He might be a rapist, or a mass murderer.'

'If there's no news of her by tomorrow,' Ross promised, 'we'll refer the matter to the police again.'

They had already made their farewells to Ross's friends, and immediately after lunch they left Aix for the long drive back to Puit de Mirabeau.

'We'll have to start thinking seriously about wedding plans,' Ross said suddenly out of a long silence. 'Do you have any strong feelings about *where* we get married? For my own part, and for various reasons, I'd sooner not go back to England.'

Claire shook her head. 'I don't mind where. My only relations are Wanda and her parents. Though I suppose Auntie Alice would be hurt if I didn't——'

'In that case we'll invite them over here for the ceremony. Claire...' his voice dropped into huskiness '...I want us to be married as soon as possible. You don't have any objection to that?'

Again she shook her head. 'No,' she said shyly. 'I'd like it to be as soon as possible too.' And in laughing protest, 'Ross, *do* keep both hands on the wheel—and look where you're going!'

'Almost home, my love.'

Claire had drifted into a contented doze, but at Ross's words she was swiftly awake. Home—how marvellous that sounded! When she had first seen the Moulin Gris she had felt such a strong sense of identification with the lovely old building. But she had never dreamed that some day it would be *her* home.

Their route to the mill took them past the Pierrepointes' field, and simultaneously they exclaimed, 'The caravan! She's back!'

Ross swung the Citroën through the field gate, and, as they bumped across the field, Claire's eyes strained for the first sight of her cousin. As Ross braked she scrambled from the car and ran for the caravan steps.

'It's locked,' she discovered disappointedly. 'There's no one here.'

'You have a key, though?'

'Yes, thank goodness. That's the one thing I did take with me.' She unlocked the door, and Ross followed her inside.

Propped up in a conspicuous position was an envelope, addressed to Claire in her cousin's familiar writing. She tore the envelope open and scanned the contents.

According to Wanda, Provence did not agree with her. The food was too strongly flavoured, the wines upset her stomach. She'd had enough and couldn't wait to get back to work and 'A lulu of a story—not to mention exquisite revenge'. 'But I don't want to cramp your style,' the note read, 'so my friend has offered me a lift back to England. Keep the van, with my blessing. You're totally unaware of it, of course, you little innocent, but you've more than earned it.' This last remark was followed by a string of exclamation marks. What on earth did Wanda mean by that?

'Well, I'll be...' Claire sank down on to the nearest bunk and stared unseeingly before her.

'Am *I* allowed to know what it says?' Ross enquired.

'Of course.' Claire still felt stunned. But she was not so *distraite* as to let him see Wanda's message for himself and the remarks about a story which revealed Wanda as a journalist. Instead, she read aloud an edited version.

'Pretty damned inconsiderate of her,' he remarked, 'to go off and leave you like this. She wasn't to know you'd be staying on. You might have had to drive all the way back to England on your own.'

'Never mind.' Claire waved this consideration aside. 'At least she's safe. Now we can get on with our own lives.'

Ross seemed much struck by this notion. 'What a good idea,' he breathed suggestively, advancing playfully upon her. But with a laugh she fended him off.

'Not here!' she protested.

'No? Well, perhaps you're right. Those bunk beds don't look as if they'd leave much room for manoeuvring.'

They surprised Madame Pierrepointe in the middle of her chores. But when they apprised her of their news she put down her household implements at once. For any satisfactory conversation, it seemed, needed both hands free to add emphasis.

'A wedding? *Mon Dieu!* Her good-natured face was wreathed in smiles. 'But what a house-cleaning there must be!' Already her housewifely instincts were turned towards practicalities.

'But first, *madame*,' Ross told her, 'there will be the party. Originally,' he explained to Claire, 'it was planned to celebrate the publication of my latest book. But now, more importantly, it will introduce my fiancée to my friends.'

Claire was still a little nervous at this prospect. But the dinner party was planned for two weeks hence, and the sun was a great tranquilliser. The days that followed passed in a haze of well-being. Long, slow days, when it was so enjoyable to be alive that nothing else could possibly matter.

And then there were the nights. Nights spent in Ross's arms, nights of sensuous love that tightened the physical and emotional bonds that drew her even closer to him. Nights during which they explored and learned each other's bodies, finding new and wonderful ways in which to delight each other.

On the day of the party Claire's nerves returned. She was far from confident about her own ability to stay afloat in a torrent of dinner-party French. As far as she knew she and Ross would be the only English people there.

Ross had his own concerns. 'I hope the weather is going to hold out—at least until after tonight,' he said. 'There's a change forecast.'

Claire took immense pains with her appearance that evening, brushing her long hair until it shone like molten copper, falling loose to well below her shoulders. Ross's eyes, words and lips rewarded her for her pains.

'You look like a Pre-Raphaelite dream of beauty,' he told her huskily between kisses. 'I *knew* that dress was right for you. God,' he groaned, 'if only all those people weren't arriving at any moment!'

'Well, really!' she teased him laughingly. 'If you think I've spent the last two hours perfecting my appearance, just for you to undo all my work——'

'*I* shall spend the whole evening looking forward to undoing it,' he assured her.

'Oh, no, you won't,' she contradicted, still teasing him but loving his denials. 'The minute your guests arrive you'll forget all about——'

'Want to bet?' he growled. And indeed, all evening she was conscious of his gaze following her. And whenever their eyes met, which they did frequently, she coloured, seeing in his the promise of the night-time hours ahead.

The guests had arrived at the sophisticated hour of nine, and Claire found herself in surroundings that she had only seen before in the pages of the *Tatler* or *Homes and Gardens*.

A candlelit table had been set out on the still warm flagstones of the rear terrace, where twenty people began the proceedings by drinking champagne.

Pierre Bonnard and his sister Marie were among the first to arrive, and were to stay overnight. Claire was conscious of Ross's watchful gaze as she greeted Pierre, and her reproving grimace at him brought a shamefaced smile of acknowledgement. A *little* jealously in one's lover *could* be flattering, she was discovering.

She was introduced to the St Clouds. Madeleine St Cloud was considerably younger than her husband, and, as Claire had feared, she detected a distinct air of pique emanating from Ross's erstwhile and now supplanted hostess.

At last, when everyone had arrived, they took their places at the long table, Ross at its head, Claire at the foot. The flickering candlelight made ruby fire of the red wine served with the first course.

Afterwards Claire could scarcely remember what she had eaten. All her concentration was on the conversation. Most of Ross's friends spoke English, but as the discussion became more animated they tended to lapse into their native tongue.

With the end of the meal, a toast was proposed by his friends to Ross's current publication, a thriller with its roots in the twin worlds of skiing and espionage. And then Ross stood to make his own announcement.

'Tonight, my friends, you have all met Claire. But until this moment she has not been introduced to you as my fiancée. For Claire has made me the happiest man in France by promising to marry me—as soon as possible,' he added in a slightly different tone, which was perhaps only perceptible to Claire.

She blushed, and then blushed even more deeply when the guests' glasses were raised to her. But she had not missed Madeleine St Cloud's swift intake of breath and the hostile glances of at least one other woman at the table.

The weather had begun to change while they were still eating. Now and again a fugitive wind blew at the candles and the tablecloth flapped and billowed, spilling wine glasses.

'I think,' said Pierre Bonnard, 'that we can shortly expect the Sacre Vent.'

'The mistral,' Ross explained for Claire's benefit. 'It happens two or three times a year. Every problem in Provence is blamed on the Sacre Vent. It can blow for as long as two weeks on end and is cited as an extenuating circumstance in crimes of violence. It uproots trees, overturns cars, smashes windows. It drives people—and animals—mad.'

There was no formal separation of men and women as the meal ended. Instead, as the sky grew darker, they all drifted back into the house. After a while the guests with journeys to make began to disperse, until at last only Pierre, his sister and the St Clouds were left.

Raoul St Cloud, a quiet man, had contributed very little to the dinner-table conversation, but now, with less competition for his host's attention, he opened up.

'You are a sly dog, my friend,' he observed between sips of the brandy he had accepted.

'Oh?' Ross raised his eyebrows and everyone looked questioningly at Raoul. 'How's that? Because I've got myself engaged, you mean?' And with a swift smile at Claire, 'It was all very sudden, I assure you. I haven't been hiding anything from my friends.'

'Not about that, perhaps,' Raoul conceded. 'But it seems we have been entertaining in our midst a celebrity greater than we realised.'

Claire, watching Ross, saw him stiffen. Not just his body but his face. Every feature was suddenly hard and still.

'Oh?' he said, warily this time. 'And precisely what does that mean?'

Raoul St Cloud seemed unaware of any tension in the atmosphere as lazily he swirled the brandy in its huge balloon glass and stared into its amber depths. 'You know, my friends,' he said, 'that I have many business interests in England. And to me regularly are sent the English newspapers. Many of these papers have the colour supplements. And this Sunday past, when I open one of them, lo and behold, what do I see?'

He looked around, and the result of his dramatic pause could not have been more effective.

There were various murmurs of curiosity from his audience, including one of protest from his wife, 'You 'ave told me nothing of this, *mon cher*.'

'I don't know,' Ross said harshly. 'What *did* you see?'

Raoul St Cloud rose from his chair. 'Wait,' he said, 'I have it in my room. I will fetch it. To see it is better than any description of mine.'

Ross rose too. 'If you don't mind,' he said, 'I'll come with you.'

'Oh,' Madeleine St Cloud pouted, 'and deprive the rest of us of this . . . *je ne sais quoi*?' She turned to Claire. 'Are you not also full of curiosity, of fear? That your new fiancé should have such dark secrets from you?'

Claire *was* curious, but not for the world would she admit it to this woman who seemed intent only on spite. She shook her head. 'I'm sure there isn't anything about Ross that could ever worry me.'

She had expected a smile of acknowledgement from Ross for her loyalty, but it was not forthcoming. Instead he stalked from the room in Raoul's wake.

After a few moments of idle speculation the other three guests fell into desultory conversation about things, places and people unknown to Claire. But she did not really mind. Her whole concern was for what was going on upstairs. What on earth had the English Sunday papers to say about Ross Savage—other than perhaps a review of his latest book?

Yes, surely that must be it. Perhaps it was an unfavourable review. But, if so, why had Raoul appeared so impressed, so mysterious?

For the first time since Raoul had opened the subject, Claire felt a little niggle of worry.

When at last Ross returned he was alone. And Claire, looking up at him and meeting his eyes as he descended the open staircase, felt a chill run through her. His stare was as cold as that of any basilisk, and it *seemed* to be for her. In a tightly clenched hand he carried a rolled-up magazine.

'Madeleine, Pierre, Marie,' he addressed his guests, 'at the risk of appearing discourteous, could I ask you to leave us? I wish to speak to Claire—alone.'

Why, Claire wondered, could he not have summoned her to their room?

He waited in silence as his guests, with curious looks at him and at Claire, mounted the stairs and disappeared into their various rooms. And even after the doors had closed behind them he remained silent. It was as though, she thought anxiously, watching his face, he was fighting some frightful internal battle—a battle he seemed to be losing.

'Ross?' She stood up and moved towards him. 'What is it? What's wrong?'

An upraised hand fended her off and a sound escaped him. The closest description was that of laughter. But oh, what a choked, bitter sound! 'What's wrong?' he scoffed. 'Did you really think,' he went on harshly, 'that I wouldn't find out?'

'Find out? Find out what? I don't understand.' So why was a cold fear creeping through her limbs, a faint dreadful suspicion stealing upon her?

'Surely you must have realised that some French people take the English newspapers? I do myself from time to time. It was bound to get back to me sooner or later.'

'Ross, I . . .'

'And what the hell did you hope to gain by agreeing to marry me? I wouldn't describe you as naïve. And yet if you'd had any sense you'd have been out of here well before publication date. Or did you think *sex* would cover a multitude of sins?'

'Ross, will you please tell me what I'm supposed to have done? Because I haven't——'

'As if you didn't know!' he said contemptuously. He flung the curled-up copy of the magazine on to a table, and Claire saw how his grasp had creased and mangled its pages. 'Well, there you are, the result of your duplicity, your treachery. I'm sure you can recall every Judas word—and how much did the Pharisees of journalism pay *you*? But by all means read it. Take what satisfaction you can from seeing your words in print. And then get the hell out of my house—and out of my life!'

He turned on his heel and strode for the stairs, while a dazed and speechless Claire watched until he disappeared from view and she heard the awful finality of a closed—and locked—door.

For a moment she could not move. Then she crept towards the table and with shaking hands picked up the despised and discarded magazine.

At first, as she turned its crumpled pages, her mystification increased. But then she reached the centrefold.

'Oh, no!' She didn't realise she had spoken aloud. And then, her legs suddenly giving under her, she sank to the floor, the magazine spread out before her.

The title of the feature leaped off the page at her in familiar words: "TIRED OF KISSING". And the photographs that illustrated it. They were her own—of the Moulin Gris, exteriors, interiors, the beautiful blue bedroom, and of Ross, the one she had taken at the Sunday market.

It didn't take much intelligence to guess how the newspaper had come by its copies. Wanda.

'Oh, Wanda, how *could* you?' Once more she groaned aloud. This explained the cryptic comment in her cousin's note: "Keep the van . . . you've more than earned it." Earned it by the photographs she had so gullibly allowed her cousin to take for developing.

And that was what Ross must think too. That Claire had been a willing collaborator, providing the pictures that accompanied the article. How was she to convince him otherwise?

But first, before she even made any attempt, she might as well know the worst. She forced herself to read the words that danced blurrily on the page before her.

Ross Savage, reclusive writer of bestsellers, has been tracked down to his Provençal retreat, a converted watermill at Puit de Mirabeau. Here, in the name of verisimilitude for his sensational thrillers, he pursues dangerous and macho pastimes.

But despite the virility of his heroes, and the sexual opulence of his blue bedroom, Ross Savage leads a celibate existence. For the dishy Mr Savage has more than his whereabouts to keep secret—namely his former existence, his alter ego as the idol of stage and screen.

Yes, before he rejected the world of glitz and glamour, Ross Savage—his real name, incidentally—was better known as Graison Martell, the heart-throb of drooling women from sixteen to sixty.

Because of his stunning good looks Graison Martell was always cast in roles of erotic tension. He was always kissing women—and more than kissing them! He played lustier and even more improbable lovers than the apparently tireless James Bond.

But, incredible as it may seem, Graison Martell tired of his involvements, on screen and off, with nubile, lusting women. Graison Martell ran away, discarding the contact lenses that turned his grey eyes to that intense blue beloved of his fans. He let his hair grow out to its natural colour and became—Ross Savage, shunning all publicity, with only his editor knowing and sworn to secrecy about his retreat.

There was more in this vein, but Claire, her tongue cleaving to the roof of her mouth and her body still numb with shock, had read enough.

Graison Martell! Ross was Graison Martell. No wonder there had been that faint sense of familiarity! Even though she had only seen blurred newspaper photographs. And then of course there was the change of hair and eye colouring. No wonder she hadn't recognised him! But she'd even said to Wanda... Oh, how her cousin must have been laughing up her sleeve!

On legs that threatened to give way again any moment, she climbed the stairs and tapped on Ross's door. There was no answer. Her mouth was still dry and she had to moisten her lips before she could speak.

'Ross!' she called softly, aware of possible listening ears in adjacent rooms, and then, a little louder, 'Ross, please! I have to talk to you.'

She heard footsteps aproaching the door and braced herself for the confrontation. But instead of the door's opening, she heard his voice, hard despite its low pitch.

'But *I* have nothing more to say to *you*.'

As Claire contemplated persistence, a door to her right opened and Madeleine St Cloud, clad in filmy nightdress and négligé, looked out. She regarded Claire with a supercilious arching of her beautiful brows and then withdrew. But it was enough. Claire would *not* plead with Madeleine as an interested listener.

Slowly she descended the stairs. Thank God she had the motor-caravan to retreat to. She didn't know what she would have done without it.

But then, she reflected miserably, as she trudged down the unlit lane to the field, her dress and high heels totally unsuitable wear for the trip, if it had not been for the motor-caravan—and Wanda's machinations—she would not have been in this situation in the first place.

The weather was still deteriorating. She shivered. The temperature must have dropped by about twenty degrees since dinner and the wind was gusting more and more often. One such gust almost had her off her feet, and it was a relief to reach the van and climb inside.

Now that she no longer had the elements to contend with she could give more attention to her personal plight. She saw it all now. Wanda had known all along where to find the former Graison Martell, but she had needed someone unknown to him to infiltrate his home and get her the information she needed. She could not have known, of course, how completely Claire would become involved with him. That had been a bonus, and the photographs too. It wouldn't matter a damn to Wanda that her cousin's involvement was to end in heartbreak.

The numbness of shock had passed now, and the full horror of her situation overtook her. The happiness of the past two weeks, the promise of future happiness—all had been swept away by her cousin's ruthless self-advancement. Claire felt as though she must drown in her own tears.

And then the thunder began—a long way off at first, from the direction of the Côte d'Azur, together with spasmodic flickers of lightning.

The storm reached Puit de Mirabeau in the dark and early hours of the morning with a clap that shook the whole caravan. In the distance Claire thought she could hear Wolf barking. The storm seemed to be directly above the van. And for an hour or more, while Claire, curled into a ball, fought against her shredded nerves, the thunder rolled and exploded and lightning floodlit the valley. She had always hated and feared storms, and there would be no one to care a damn if she was struck by lightning—or by a thunderbolt.

Finally it began to pour with rain, crashing on the roof and rattling against the windowpane, the caravan rocking crazily to the wind's violent assaults.

At first she thought the loud battering noise was part of the storm, but then she realised someone was beating on the door of the caravan. Her heart in her mouth, cautiously she peered through a gap in the curtains. This was such an isolated place, and there were often hideous stories in the media about lone women campers being attacked.

At first her limited view showed her only a tall dark shape. But then a searing flash of lightning identified the figure as that of Ross. She stumbled to the door, and promptly had it torn from her hand by a violent gust of wind. The hinges were not equal to the strain, and next moment the whole door was carried away across the field. But it didn't matter. Nothing mattered. Ross had come in search of her. He'd had time to cool off, to realise . . .

'Oh, Ross, thank God!' She held out welcoming hands, but he brushed past her into the van.

'Get your things together. You're coming back to the house.'

'Yes,' she said joyfully. 'Oh, yes, of course!' She hurried to do his bidding. This wasn't the time or the place for a reconciliation, with the door wrenched off and the wind invading every corner.

He took the hastily packed bag, then hustled her down the steps and into his car, flinging the case into the back. As they set off across the field the little car rocked crazily, buffeted by the wind.

Ross had said nothing more since his unexpected arrival and he was just a dark outline beside her. Claire put a hand on his arm.

'Ross, darling, I'm so glad . . .' But her voice trailed away as an impatient jerk of his arm dislodged her hand.

'Don't get the wrong idea,' he rasped. 'Nothing's changed.'

'Then why——?'

'Because, dammit, this weather is going to get worse, and I wouldn't leave my worst enemy exposed to its whims in the middle of a field. It may have escaped your notice, but you were parked close to some large trees. Besides, it's a wonder that vehicle hasn't already tipped over.'

'It almost did once or twice,' Claire told him. 'But oh, Ross, when you came for me, I thought you'd realised I couldn't have——'

'I told you, nothing's changed. You can stay at the house until the mistral's run its course, but that's all.'

Then why hadn't he left her where she was, Claire brooded miserably, instead of raising her hopes like that, only to have them plummet disastrously again? She would rather have taken her chances with the elements than with Ross's angry scorn.

The strength of the wind meant that he had to put a supportive hand under her elbow as they mounted the front steps of the Moulin Gris. But his touch was painfully hard and totally impersonal, and the moment they were through the door he released her, dropping her bag to the floor.

Without looking directly at her he gestured towards the stairs. He said curtly, 'You can use the blue room again.' And then he was gone, into his study, closing the door behind him.

The blue bedroom, Claire thought drearily as she lugged her bag up the stairs. Although latterly they had used Ross's bed, the blue room had been the scene of their first lovemaking. Was he being deliberately cruel? There were other bedrooms. She knew she would never be able to sleep.

To her surprise she found she *had* slept, and heavily, weighed down by unhappiness and the fatigue of a disturbed night. It was late when she woke and looked out on the effects of the storm damage on earth that had been baked for weeks. All around wraiths of steam were rising, and there was a continuous hissing sound as the heat of a new day dried the undergrowth.

And still the wind blew, though perhaps not quite as violently. For as she continued to look out of the window two cars came slowly round the side of the house. She recognised them as the vehicles in which Pierre Bonnard and his sister and the St Clouds had arrived. The last of Ross's guests were leaving. She was alone with him.

Claire was not without courage, and she knew she would have to fight if she wanted a future with Ross. She had to try again, to make one more attempt at least to convince him of her innocence.

As she watched the disappearing cars she saw Ross, having speeded his guests, come back into the house. She heard him coming up the stairs, and tensed as his footsteps paused at her door.

There was a peremptory knock. Then, without waiting for an answer, he said coldly, 'There's some breakfast for you downstairs if you want it.' And before she could cross the room he had moved on and into his own room.

She waited, fully expecting to hear him lock his door, as he had done last night. But when he did not a reckless plan of action came to her. Feverishly she scrambled into bra and panties, topping them with a thin robe. As an afterthought, she dug out Wanda's farewell note from her handbag and thrust it into the robe pocket. Then, emerging from her room, she tiptoed across the landing.

Outside Ross's door she stopped, and for the first time the full realisation of what she was about to do made fear scud down her spine and made her stomach churn. But it was do or die.

Her hand closed over the door-knob. Then with a swift movement she was in the room, closing the door behind her—and locking it, the key going into the deep cleft between her breasts.

Ross was not in the bedroom, but the sound of running water gave her the clue to his whereabouts. Taking a deep steadying breath, she walked into the bathroom.

Standing beneath the shower, his back turned to her, Ross was totally unaware of her presence.

As for Claire, although she had seen him naked many times, there was an additional *frisson* in the knowledge of the coming confrontation, in not knowing how he would react.

Then a chance glance towards the mirror must have shown him her reflection, for he swung round and for a moment almost lost his footing. He did not—as a woman might have done—grab for the nearest towel. Instead he confronted her in all his male magnificence, and Claire had to put out a hand to the door-frame to steady herself against suddenly reeling senses.

Fury made granite of his features. 'What the hell do you think you're doing? Get out of here!'

Claire swallowed nervously, but, 'No, I'm *not* leaving! Not until you've listened to me and given me a chance——'

'To tell me more lies?' he grated. 'Some hope. *Get out!*' And he advanced threateningly towards her.

But Claire stood her ground, despite what the sight of him was doing to her. 'I want a fair hearing,' she said with greater hardiness than she felt.

Now he did reach for a towel. Wrapping it sarong-wise around him, he brushed past her into the bedroom. 'Then if *you* won't leave *I* will.'

As the bedroom door failed to open, he swung round, his mouth set in grim lines, his eyes grey flints. He spoke softly but with an ominous edge to his voice. 'Unlock this door, Claire.'

She was trembling in every limb at her own temerity. She would never have dared to stand up to Joe in this way. But she would *not* be vanquished by Ross's anger. She had everything to fight for. Somehow her legs managed to get her as far as the bed. She sank down on the side of it and regarded him, her green eyes appealing.

'Surely it won't do any harm just to listen to me?'

'I listened to you once before,' he reminded her icily.

'I was telling you the truth then—and I'm telling it now,' Claire told him. 'I'm not a journalist. I had nothing to do with that article being printed and I——'

'Do you deny that they were *your* photos?' His tone was sarcastic and his rapier-sharp gaze held a warning of violence scarcely held in check.

'No, but I can ex——'

'Right, then! *Give me the key, Claire—now!*' Fists clenched he advanced upon her. 'Where is it?' he demanded.

She held his glance defiantly, but an involuntary little movement of her hand betrayed the key's hiding-place.

'I see!' His mouth twisted with derision. 'Do you think *that* will prevent me taking it from you?'

'Ross,' she pleaded, 'please let me . . .'

But he was standing over her. 'I'll give you until a count of five to hand over that key. And then . . .'

'And then?' she challenged him, chin stubbornly tilted.

'And then I'm going to *take* it from you.'

'It won't be easy,' she warned him. 'You'd better be prepared to——'

'Oh, I'm prepared, Claire,' he said softly. 'I'm eminently well prepared.' He began to count. 'One, two——'

'You're wasting your time,' she told him. 'You might just as well——'

'Three, four——'

'Just as well give me a chance——'

'Five!' His hands bit into her shoulders, his eyes blazed with fury, *'Give me that key!'*

Claire was small, but she was wiry, and she fought with all her strength, using nails, fists, feet and even teeth against his masculine strength. If this had been Joe, she thought with vague surprise, she would not have dared to engage in physical combat. In a temper he would not have scorned to use *his* fists on *her*. But Ross, despite his anger, would not stoop to such violence. He was merely relying on his superior strength and staying power.

That superior strength finally had her clamped against his body with one arm, while his free hand hovered at the neckline of her robe.

'Are you going to admit defeat?' he demanded.

'No!' she spat back at him. And as that hand still hovered, 'Well, what are you waiting for?' she challenged him. 'I'm at your mercy, aren't I?'

Still he hesitated, and, unable to fight now, Claire became aware of other things. The fact that in the struggle he had lost his towel. She became aware too of the heat of the body touching hers, the subtle smell of the cologne he always wore. A sensuous little shiver ran through her. She groaned softly and ran her tongue over suddenly dry lips.

'Stop it, Claire!' he snapped. 'Stop that! Don't try your seductive wiles on me!'

'Is that what I'm doing?' she murmured, studying his suddenly heated face, aware of an interesting unrest in the body moulded against hers.

'You know you are, dammit.' His gaze roamed the flushed beauty of her face. 'That's what all this is about, isn't it? You deliberately hid that key there.' His fingers brushed her breasts. 'You *wanted* me to try and get it. Because you know damned well that once I touched you——'

'Yes?' she breathed.

'And you've succeeded, blast you.' His arms tightened even more painfully, but not just to restrain her now. 'You *knew* what it would do to me, even though I know you're a treacherous little bitch.'

'But I'm not,' she whispered, 'as you'd know if you'd only take the trouble to find out.'

He was breathing hard, his chest rising and falling. 'I wish I could believe you,' he muttered huskily. 'But how can I——?'

'It would take a few days, but you could check with the newspaper that ran the feature.' And then, quickly, because for a moment at least she had his full attention, 'I was made use of, Ross. Oh, I was a fool not to tell you about my cousin—and for letting her dupe me. But it *was* foolishness, Ross, not deceit.'

'What *about* your cousin?' he demanded. But he had not moved away from her. It was as if he could *not* move.

Frankly, Claire met his gaze. 'Wanda *is* a journalist. But she was supposed to be on holiday. I never dreamed she was after a story. She invited me to join her because she said I needed a break, but I realise now it was for her own ends. *She* needed *me*. Because I was unknown to you—and she needed my camera. I let her take those photos for developing in good faith. Ross, read this. I didn't fully understand it at the time, but I do now. Oh, yes, I do now.' She handed him Wanda's note and watched as he read it. Watched his darkening brow as he muttered certain phrases aloud: 'a lulu of a story'; 'exquisite revenge'; 'totally unaware'; 'you little innocent'.

'What's your cousin's full name?' he demanded harshly.

'Wanda Hedley.'

'Wanda Hedley,' he repeated. Abruptly he released her, and Claire knew she had gone pale. She'd lost her gamble. While he held her so closely there had been a chance. Yes, she *had* counted on the sexual chemistry between them to ensure her a hearing, counted on his physical need of her to overcome his doubts and suspicions.

'Wanda Hedley,' he said again, beginning to pace the room. 'That hard-faced... That explains everything. She was one of those damned women who made my life such a hell. I lost count of the number of times I refused to give her an interview. And then she had the gall to break into my house, the colossal nerve to try and seduce me when other means had failed. And when I threw her out—neck and crop—made her understand in no uncertain terms that her charm had failed her... I swear I've never heard such language from a woman, such spite, such threats. It sickened me. No wonder I never saw your cousin! She knew I'd recognise her the minute I clapped eyes on her.'

'I *did* wonder why she always steered clear of you,' Claire admitted miserably. 'I even asked her about it, but she denied knowing you. Of course,' she said bitterly, 'I should have remembered—Wanda never had any compunction about telling lies, even to those closest to her.'

Ross scarcely seemed to hear her words. 'It was women like your cousin who finally sickened me of my career, made me see the falseness, the shallowness of the life I was leading. And I blamed myself. God gave me dark hair and grey eyes, yet there I was, allowing my hair to be *bleached*, wearing contact lenses because "blue eyes had more sex appeal." God, how demeaning! My only excuse is that I was young and ambitious when it all began, and once something's begun you tend to let it ride. And,' he added grimly, 'there was the money. But when I finally realised how much I was debasing myself... When I lost the woman I loved, just because other women saw me as a sex symbol—because I could never call my life my own—because of hard-boiled harpies like your cousin...'

Claire stood up, her shoulders slumped defeatedly. 'Well, now you know the truth. And that was all I wanted, to be allowed to tell the full story. I suppose you still don't believe me, but I *wasn't* a party to Wanda's plans. Here,' she thrust her fingertips into her bra, 'take your key. I——'

Ross moved swiftly. His hand stayed the movement of hers. 'Wait!' And then, with a grin, 'I rather think that's *my* prerogative.' His fingers replaced hers beneath the lacy edge of her bra. But instead of searching for the key they began to caress, to tease, while his free hand slid around her waist, pulling her to him.

'Ross?' she breathed, looking up at him questioningly, scarcely daring to believe. 'Does...does this mean——?'

'It means, my love,' he told her ruefully, 'that I owe you an apology for doubting you. I've finally learned to tell the difference between truth and lies, between dross and pure gold. And you, my sweet Claire, are pure gold.'

His lips brushed sensuously over hers. 'And you're courageous too,' he murmured wonderingly. 'I think it was your courage that began to convince me, even before your words could—even before you showed me your cousin's revealing little note. Knowing how much you feared physical violence. And yet you were willing to put yourself in a position that could have turned nasty.'

'With any other man, maybe,' she agreed. 'But I always knew *you* would never hurt me, however angry you were.'

The exploring fingers had finally come upon the key, and now he withdrew it, holding it aloft and looking at it with a comical expression contorting his features. For an instant he pressed it to his lips as though savouring the warmth her flesh had given to the metal. Then, with a sudden movement, he threw it into the furthest corner of the room.

'Let the door *stay* locked,' he said huskily as he picked her up and carried her back to the bed. And— a long time later, 'Who *said* I was "tired of kissing"?'

YOU <u>CAN</u> AFFORD THAT HOLIDAY!

Great savings can be made when you book your next holiday – whether you want to go skiing, take a luxury cruise, or lie in the Mediterranean sun – the Holiday Club offers you the chance to receive **FREE HOLIDAY SPENDING MONEY** worth up to 10% of the cost of your holiday.

All you have to do is choose a holiday from one of the major holiday companies including Thomson, Cosmos, Horizon, Cunard, Kuoni, Jetsave and many more.

Just call us* and ask if the holiday company you wish to book with is included.

HOW MUCH SPENDING MONEY WILL I RECEIVE?

The amount you receive is based on the basic price of your holiday. Add up the total cost for all holiday-makers listed on your booking form – excluding surcharges, supplements, insurance, car hire or special excursions where these are not included in the basic cost, and after any special reductions which may be offered on the holiday – then compare the total with the price bands below:-

YOUR TOTAL BASIC HOLIDAY PRICE FOR ALL PASSENGERS	HOLIDAY SPENDING MONEY
£ 200 449	£ 20
450 649	30
650 849	40
850 1099	60
1100 1499	80
1500 1999	100 ...
... 8500 or more	500

Having paid the balance of your holiday 10 weeks prior to travelling, your **FREE HOLIDAY SPENDING MONEY** will be sent to you with your tickets in the form of a cheque from the Holiday Club approximately 7-10 days before departure.

We reserve the right to decline any booking at our discretion. All holidays are subject to availability and the terms and conditions of the tour operators.

HOW TO BOOK

1. CHOOSE YOUR HOLIDAY from one of the major holiday companies brochures, making a note of the flight and hotel codes.

2. PHONE IT THROUGH* with your credit card details for the deposit, or full payment if within 10 weeks of departure and quote P&M Ref: H&C/MBC185. Your holiday must be booked with the Holiday Club before 30.6.92 and taken before 31.12.93.

3. SEND THE BOOKING FORM from the brochure to the address above, marking the top right hand corner of the booking form with P&M Ref: H&C/MBC185.

If you prefer to book by post or wish to pay the deposit by cheque, omit stage 2 and simply mail your booking to us. We will contact you if your holiday is not available.

Send to: The Holiday Club
P O Box 155 Leicester LE1 9GZ
* Tel No. (0533) 513377
Mon – Fri 9 am – 8 pm, Sat 9 am – 4 pm
Sun and Bank Holidays 10 am – 4 pm

CONDITIONS OF OFFER

Most people like to take out holiday insurance to cover for loss of possessions or injury. It is a condition of the offer that Page & Moy will arrange suitable insurance for you – further details are available on request. In order to provide comprehensive cover insurance will become payable upon confirmation of your holiday. The insurance premium is not refundable on cancellation.

Free Holiday Spending Money is not payable if travel on the holiday does not take place.

The Holiday Club is run by Page & Moy Ltd Britain's largest single location travel agent and a long standing member of ABTA.

N.B. Any contractual arrangements are between yourselves and the tour operators, not Mills & Boon Ltd.

ABTA 99529 Page & Moy Ltd Reg No. 115114

WIN A LUXURY CRUISE

TO THE MEDITERRANEAN
AND BLACK SEA

Last month we told you all about the fabulous cruise you could win just by entering our competition and sending in two tokens from November and December Romances.

For the lucky winner the popular cruise ship the Kareliya will be a floating hotel visiting eight exciting ports of call, including Lisbon, Athens and Istanbul.

For your chance to win this fabulous cruise for two people just answer these three questions and the tie-breaker which follows:

Which country is renowned for its delicious port? ....

Which volcano is situated on the island of Sicily? ....

Which Turkish city sits at the mouth of the Bosphorus? ....

Tie-Breaker. Tell us in no more than 15 words which romantic partner you would like to take on a cruise with you and why ....

....

....

Name: ....

Address: ....

....Postcode: ....

Are you a Reader Service subscriber?   Yes ☐   No ☐

Send your entry, together with two tokens, a red one from November and a blue one from December Romances by 31st January 1992 to:

Holiday Competition   Mills & Boon Reader Service
P.O. Box 236   Thornton Road   Croydon   Surrey   CR9 3RU

Next month's Romances

Each month, you can choose from a world of variety in romance with Mills & Boon. These are the new titles to look out for next month.

DESPERATE MEASURES Sara Craven

STRANGER FROM THE PAST Penny Jordan

FATED ATTRACTION Carole Mortimer

A KIND OF MAGIC Betty Neels

A CANDLE FOR THE DEVIL Susanne McCarthy

TORRID CONFLICT Angela Wells

LAST SUMMER'S GIRL Elizabeth Barnes

DESERT DESTINY Sarah Holland

THE CORSICAN GAMBIT Sandra Marton

GAMES FOR SOPHISTICATES Diana Hamilton

SUBSTITUTE HUSBAND Margaret Callaghan

MIRROR IMAGE Melinda Cross

LOVE BY DESIGN Rosalie Ash

IN PURSUIT OF LOVE Jayne Bauling

NO LAST SONG Ann Charlton

STARSIGN

ENIGMA MAN Nicola West

Available from Boots, Martins, John Menzies, W.H. Smith, most supermarkets and other paperback stockists.

Also available from Mills and Boon Reader Service, P.O. Box 236, Thornton Road, Croydon, Surrey CR9 3RU.